Geological Society of America
Memoir 190

Plugs and Plug Circles: A Basic Form of Patterned Ground, Cornwallis Island, Arctic Canada—Origin and Implications

A. L. Washburn
Quaternary Research Center
University of Washington
Seattle, Washington 98195

1997

Published by The Geological Society of America, Inc.
3300 Penrose Place, P.O. Box 9140, Boulder, Colorado 80301

Printed in U.S.A.

GSA Books Science Editor Abhijit Basu

Library of Congress Cataloging-in-Publication Data

Washburn, A. L. (Albert Lincoln), 1911-
Plugs and plug circles : a basic form of patterned ground, Cornwallis Island, Arctic Canada : origin and implications / A.L. Washburn.
p. cm. -- (Memoir / Geological Society of America ; 190)
Includes bibliographical references and index.
ISBN 0-8137-1190-8
1. Patterned ground--Northwest Territories--Cornwallis Island.
I. Title. II. Series: Memoir (Geological Society of America) ; 190.
GB648.15.W37 1997
551.3'8'097192--dc21 97-12288
CIP

10 9 8 7 6 5 4 3 2 1

Contents

Geological Society of America
Memoir 190
1997

Plugs and Plug Circles: A Basic Form of Patterned Ground, Cornwallis Island, Arctic Canada—Origin and Implications

ABSTRACT

Plug circles and semicircles are a type of patterned ground formed as the surface expression of plugs, which are subsurface cylindrical or more irregular soil masses extending upward from depth. Plug circles and semicircles may be sorted or nonsorted and range in diameter from a few centimeters to a meter or more.

Detailed study of the above forms on Cornwallis Island in the Canadian High Arctic demonstrates that they can occur in a variety of deposits, including beach gravels, mixed deposits, and disintegrating bedrock and that plugs terminate downward at or near the permafrost table in fines-rich soil that can be very stony or relatively free of stones. A survey of similar occurrences elsewhere shows that they are widespread in some permafrost regions in the Arctic and probably in permafrost environments more generally; whether they also develop in the absence of permafrost is problematic.

Field evidence and analysis of various hypotheses of patterned-ground origin indicate that the essential process in the origin of plug circles and related forms is differential frost heaving in a permafrost environment in which the freezing front moves not only downward from the ground surface but also upward from a permafrost table. Surfaceward seepage can be a critical companion process that explains some concentrated occurrences of plug circles and semicircles.

It appears that plug circles and plugs constitute a basic genetic type of patterned ground. Depending on environmental conditions, transitions occur from plug circles to several other types of patterned ground. With the introduction of a continuing circulatory process, some ring-bordered forms may evolve into the classical, prominent ring-bordered type of Spitsbergen.

ABBREVIATIONS

The following special abbreviations occur in this report.

AGI/G	American Geological Institute/Glossary (Bates and Jackson, 1987)
DE	Dye Experiment(s)
EB	Even-bordered (circles and related forms)
ES	Experimental Site(s)
M	Matrix (in grain-size determinations)
N	Nonsorted (patterned ground)
NRCC/G	National Research Council of Canada/ Glossary (Permafrost Subcommittee, 1988)
PCSP	Polar Continental Shelf Project
PE	Plug Excavation(s)
QL	Quaternary Isotope Laboratory, University of Washington
RB	Ring-bordered (circles and related forms)
S	Sorted (patterned ground)
TACAN (Bldg.)	Tactical Air Navigation (Bldg.)—A deactivated facility at the south end of the "road" to "Crystal City"
VOR (Site)	Visual Overhead Range
w_f	Percent water content (frozen) measured as $\frac{\text{wt. water}_f}{\text{wt. dried soil}} \times 100$

Washburn, A. L., 1997, Plugs and Plug Circles: A Basic Form of Patterned Ground, Cornwallis Island, Arctic Canada—Origin and Implications: Boulder, Colorado, Geological Society of America Memoir 190.

INTRODUCTION AND ACKNOWLEDGMENTS

This report is one of several resulting from my fieldwork in Canada's Arctic Islands, mainly in the immediate vicinity of Resolute Bay[1] on Cornwallis Island, N.W.T., in Canada's High Arctic (Figs. 1, 2, 3). Fieldwork lasting 1 to 4 months each year was carried out over the period 1981 to 1995 except in the 1993–1994 season; several days were spent at Resolute in 1995. The work was under the auspices of the famed Polar Continental Shelf Project (PCSP) of Energy, Mines and Resources Canada (now Natural Resources Canada). Other responsibilities led to some discontinuity in program effort over the years. Reports to date focus on deleveling (Washburn and Stuiver, 1985), movement in some sorted circles (Washburn, 1989), and an abstract on plugs and plug circles (Washburn, 1991). The results of 8 yr of theodolite observations of gelifluction are being prepared for publication. The present report deals with the nature, origin, and development of plugs and plug circles, a comparatively little known but fundamental variety of patterned ground and, it is suggested, a precursor of several other varieties. Figure 19, shown later, illustrates a typical plug sorted circle (the surface expression of a plug) in beach gravel.

To obtain a broad perspective on origin and possible relationship of plug circles and plugs to other types of patterned ground, hypotheses of patterned–ground origin are reviewed.

To acknowledge all those to whom I and my wife and field assistant, Tahoe, are indebted would require a chapter in itself. In particular, we are most grateful to George Hobson, former director of the PCSP; to Dr. Pierre Lapointe, his successor; and to present director Bonnie Hrycyk. Without their support and that of former PCSP managers, Jim Godden, Barry Hough, Frank Hunt, and now Dave Maloley, the work could not have been done. Of former staff, Bill Presley was very helpful. Other government agencies at Resolute whose help was also highly important included Canada's Air Weather Service and the Ministry of Transport. Buster and Cathy Welch of Fisheries Canada assisted informally. High Arctic International (operated by the late Bezal Jesudason and his wife Terry), Narwhal Arctic Services (now Frontec Arctic Services), and Aziz Kheraj (Kheraj Enterprises Ltd.) were very helpful. We also greatly appreciated the invaluable assistance of Inuit friends, George Eckalook (then chairman of the Resolute Bay Hamlet Council), Aleesuk Eckalook, Minnie and Elizabeth Allakariallak, and many others.

Colleagues and others elsewhere who have been especially helpful include Dr. Ray Thorsteinsson (Geological Survey of Canada) for very helpful discussions in the field and other information on the bedrock geology, Professor Michael Church (Department of Geography, University of British Columbia) for arranging for soil analyses to be carried out in his laboratory, and Sidney Tsang for undertaking them. Professor Ming-ko Woo (Department of Geography, McMaster University, Hamilton, Ontario, Canada) assisted in contouring Experimental Site C in 1994. Professor Minze Stuiver (Department of Geological Sciences and Quaternary Research Center [QRC], University of Washington) generously contributed numerous radiocarbon dates. Professor Bernard Hallet (Department of Geological Sciences and QRC) and his then assistants (now professor) Robert Anderson, Suzanne Anderson, and Carrington Gregory provided excellent field collaboration in 1982. Christopher Stubbs (now professor) visited Resolute in 1984 to successfully resolve some instrumentation problems. Former graduate students David McCormack and Geoffrey Clayton ably assisted me throughout much of the program. L. A. Rasmussen was responsible for summarizing much of the meteorological data; he also helped to analyze frost-heave observations at Experimental Site C. Floyd Bardsley of the Department of Geological Sciences at the University of Washington (now retired) was responsible for essentially all the drafting.

Paul Egginton (Geological Survey of Canada) and Dr. Brigitte Van Vliet-Lanoë (Centre de Géomorphologie du C.N.R.S. [Centre National de la Recherche Scientifique]) commented on an early draft of the report, and Professor Hallet made many stimulating and valuable suggestions on two later drafts. Finally, I am also very grateful to Professor James C. Walters of the Department of Earth Sciences, University of Northern Iowa, who refereed the manuscript; to Professor Emeritus Robert P. Sharp (California Institute of Technology), an old friend who urged me to shorten the original manuscript, which led to considerable curtailment in places; and to another old friend, Professor J. R. Mackay (University of British

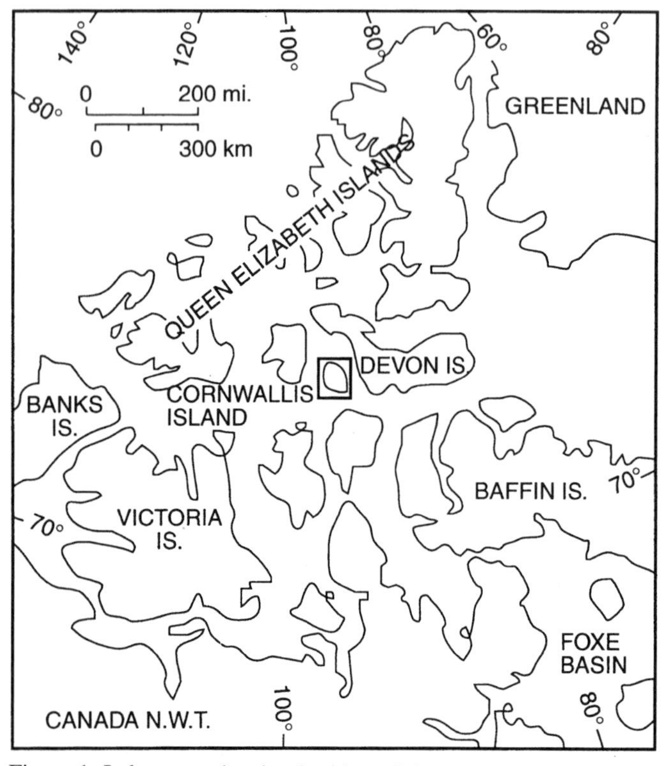

Figure 1. Index map showing location of Cornwallis Island, N.W.T.

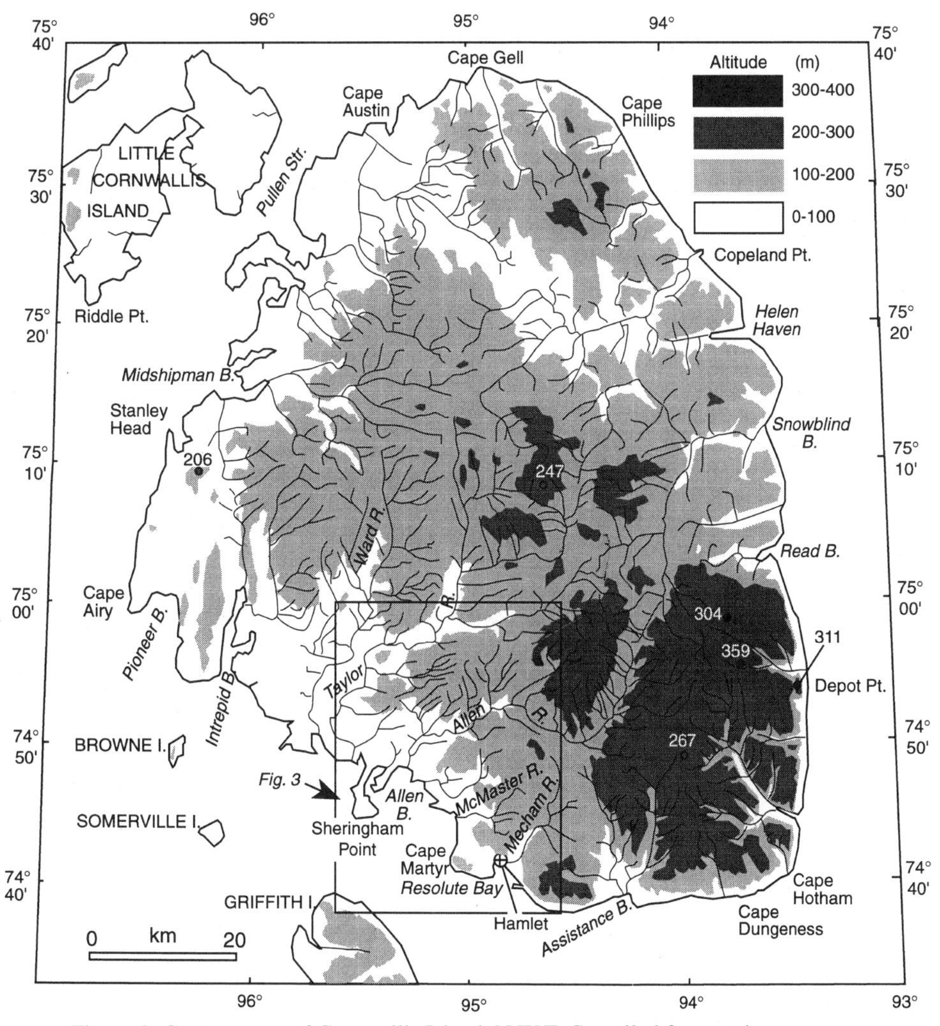

Figure 2. Contour map of Cornwallis Island, N.W.T. Compiled from various sources.

Columbia), whose pioneer work at Resolute was most perceptive (Mackay, 1953) and whose comments on the manuscript were very thoughtful and helpful.

Patra Leaming's accuracy in typing and proofreading this report was exemplary.

GENERAL

Climate

Cornwallis Island is noted for fog, low summer ceilings, possible snowfall during any month of the year, and generally inclement weather. Shirtsleeve weather is restricted to a few exceptional days a year, and some Inuit and other longtime residents of Resolute can recall a few years that had "no summer." Because of the island's relatively small size—about 7,380 km^2 (ca. 2,850 mi^2;[2] Thorsteinsson and Kerr, 1968, p. 1)—the weather reflects the influence of the surrounding open water with normally minimal sea ice in late August and in September.

Temperature, precipitation, and wind speed for 1947 through 1990 are shown in Appendix A, Table 1. The mean annual air temperature is –16.6 °C. Only July (4.0 °C) and August (1.9 °C) have mean daily temperatures above freezing. The number of annual freeze-thaw cycles averaged 11.6 for 1961 through 1970, 12.4 for 1971 through 1980, and 9.3 for 1981 through 1990. The 1947–1990 mean annual precipitation was 139.6 mm, of which 50.4 mm was rain. Fog is common from May through October and is especially prevalent in August. The monthly wind speed ranges from 20 to 24 km/h, the highest being in the fall. A maximum hourly speed of 142 km/h and gusts to 158 km/h have been recorded in November. Wind directions are predominantly from the northwest except for high gusts, which are from the east in all months except January, when they are from the north.

Soil temperatures

Soil temperatures at Resolute were discussed by Cook (1955). Among other things, he compared soil temperatures in shattered rock and gravel (as in borders of sorted circles) with those at comparable depths in finer soil (as below the central

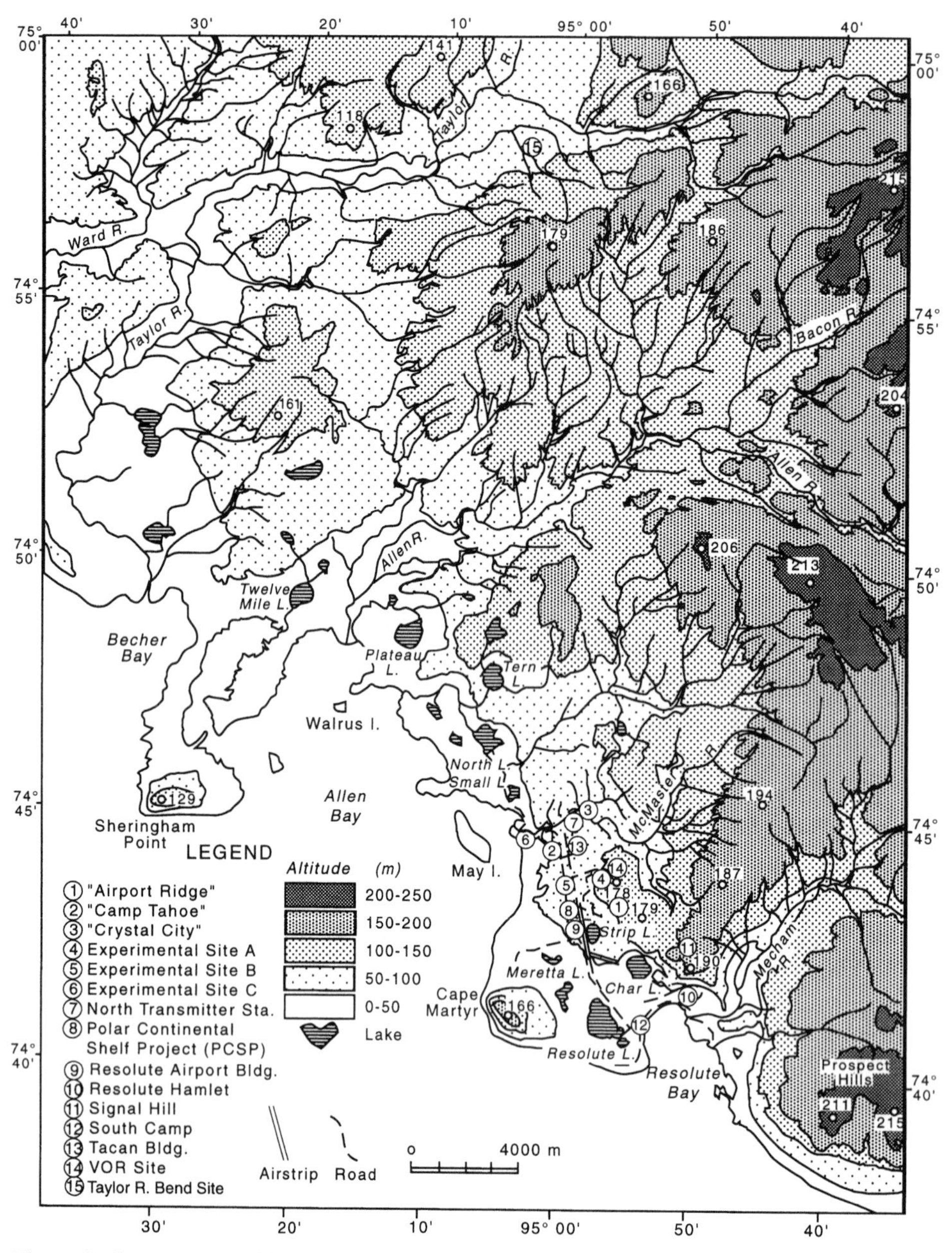

Figure 3. Contour map of Resolute area, Cornwallis Island, N.W.T., showing location of various sites. Topography modified from Energy Mines and Resources Canada (1985).

area of circles) during the freeze-up period (freeze-back) in 1955 (Cook, 1955, his Table 3, p. 246, an extract of which is included in Appendix B, Table 1).

This extract shows a zero-curtain effect as manifested by a run of identical or nearly identical temperatures within a fraction of a degree below 0 °C. Cook noted that at 20 cm (8 in.) "... in the shattered rock and gravel ... the zero curtain effect lasted 10 days, while in the clay[3] at the same depth it was prolonged to 14 days" (Cook, 1955, p. 245). Consequently, for this depth the time required for freezing of the shattered rock and gravel was 1.4 times more rapid than for the clay. The freezing rate at equal depths in these two soils increased with depth, as illustrated in Appendix B, Figure 1. The fact that the shattered rock and gravel generally froze before the clay is an important consideration in the origin of patterned ground, as Cook recognized.

Cook also showed the seasonal soil-temperature overturns in shattered rock and gravel in which the temperature gradient in the active layer becomes reversed, as illustrated for 1954 in Appendix B, Figure 2. Following maximum thaw to the base of the active layer in August, the overturn was accompanied by general upward freezing from the permafrost table as well as by downward freezing from the surface. However, surface cooling resulting in a downward-moving cooling front may also result in episodes of significant upward freezing from a frost table (as distinct from a permafrost table), as reported from elsewhere by Tarnocai (1980, p. 325–326). The importance of upward freezing is discussed later in the section "Hypotheses of Origin, Differential frost heaving and surfaceward seepage."

Freeze-thaw cycles in the ground as well as in the air at Resolute were recorded by Cook and Raiche (1962, their Table 1, p. 67), and are here included in Appendix B as Table 2. For comparison with the –2.2 to 1.1° C freeze-thaw criterion adopted by Maxwell (1980, p. 148; see Appendix A, Table 1) and excluding the annual cycle, no soil freeze-thaw cycles were recorded below a depth of 2.5 cm and only one at that depth. However, incomplete soil-temperature records at my Experimental Site A (Fig. 3), the site of a gelifluction study that will be the subject of a future report, indicate the occasional presence of one to two freeze-thaw cycles at considerable depth in addition to the annual cycle.

Geography and geology

Cornwallis Island rises to a maximum altitude of 359 m (1,148 ft) (Fig. 2) in the southeast part, which forms a high plateau with rugged topography near the southeast coast. This plateau, deeply incised in places, declines to the north and west. The south and southeast coasts rise steeply from the water, but the southwest, west, and northwest coasts are generally low lying.

The drainage is dominantly dendritic. The largest rivers drain to the west coast, extending from there into the central area of the island, especially the Allen, Taylor, and Ward Rivers, which together drain most of the central part.

The rocks range in age from Ordovician through Tertiary. Broad, gently dipping anticlines and synclines predominate, but extensive faulting has occurred, producing grabens in places, and the structure is locally complicated (Thorsteinsson, 1958, 1986; Thorsteinsson and Kerr, 1968). Carbonate rocks (dolomites, dolomitic limestones, and limestones)[4] of Ordovician and Silurian age predominate in the Resolute area (Fig. 4), but red siltstone of Devonian age occurs just to the north of Resolute in the vicinity of the river that drains into North Lake.

The available meager information on the glacial history of Cornwallis Island has been summarized by Edlund (1991, p. 9–20). Erratics and diamictons are widespread, but probable pre-Holocene submergence up to uncertain altitudes as well as gelifluction and other forms of mass wasting at most altitudes have so confused the evidence that few deposits or land forms can be identified as glacial with certainty. As a result the glacial history remains somewhat problematic. Summarizing the evidence, Edlund (1991, p. 1, 13–16) reported that field evidence and air photo interpretation suggest that Cornwallis Island was invaded by an erratic-bearing pre–Late Wisconsinan ice sheet (or ice sheets) of otherwise unknown age from the mainland and that the island was subsequently glaciated by a local ice cap.

Two models exist for the last glaciation. One is that the Queen Elizabeth Islands, including Cornwallis Island (Fig. 1), were covered with an Innutian ice sheet (Blake, 1970, p. 660–661; and others). The second model calls only for the presence of local ice caps as an alternative explanation (Edlund, 1991, p. 18). According to the latter model, the Late Wisconsinan Laurentide ice from the mainland extended almost to Cornwallis Island (A. S. Dyke and Prest, 1987, their Fig. 3, p. 258) or was coalescent with Cornwallis ice (A. S. Dyke et al., 1991, p. 42). The available evidence from nearby Griffith Island (Fig. 2) is inconclusive (A. S. Dyke, 1993, p. 138–139). In any event, waning Late Wisconsinan ice (cap?) on Cornwallis Island left striae indicating outward-moving ice along the east and south coasts and abundant ice-marginal drainage channels along major rivers draining to the east and west coasts.

In addition to the information provided by Edlund (1991, p. 16) regarding pre-Holocene emergence, the following unpublished radiocarbon dates are pertinent. A specimen of thin, fragile shell fragments from a probable glaciomarine deposit exposed on the east-facing cut bank of the Mecham River at an altitude of 24 ± 3 m revealed a ^{14}C age of 29,200 +1,400, –1,200 B.P. (Appendix C, QL-4070). The bed underlay Holocene marine shells with a date of 8280 ± 40 B.P. (Appendix C, QL-4071) near the bench top. The stratigraphy is consistent with the lower Mecham Valley being ice free at some 28,000 to 30,000 B.P. Older dates on pockets of fine-grained organic matter in the cut bank about a meter lower some 10 m upstream were 35,000 ± 1,800 B.P. (Appendix C, QL-4329) and 43,100 +3,800, –2,600 B.P. (Appendix C, QL-4328) and are more likely to be minimum only, with possibly the organics having been redeposited.

Following the most recent glaciation, Holocene emergence left beaches extending to altitudes of 80 to 100 m on low-lying coasts (Edlund, 1991, p. 11). In the Resolute area, the evidence suggests a Holocene marine limit at 120 ± 3 m, based on a sequence of radiocarbon ages and altitudes (Washburn and Stuiver, 1985, their Fig. 1, Tables 1, 2) supplemented by subsequent unpublished shell dates of 9570 ± 40 B.P. (QL 1904) and 9790 ± 50 B.P. (QL-4073) from altitudes of 113 ± 2 m and 117 ± 3 m, respectively (Appendix C). A 120-m altitude would correspond to the marine limit suggested by Edlund (1991, p. 14) and is near the 122-m level at nearby Somerset Island where a limiting minimum age of 9300 B.P. (9.3 Ka) has been obtained (A. S. Dyke, et al., 1991, p. 34; their Fig. 14C, p. 37). These ages are comparable in that Geological Survey of Canada ages are reported as 400 yr younger than the QL ages because of being normalized to a $\delta^{13}C$ of 0‰ instead of –25‰.

A variety of cold-climate soils occurs in the Resolute area, as described and mapped by Cruickshank (1971) (Fig. 5), who recognized various terrain units of Polar desert, Lithosols, and Tundra and Bog Soils. In the Cryosolic Order of the Canadian classification (Canada Soil Survey Committee, 1978, p. 63–68), these soils include Regosolic Static (and Turbic) Cryosols and Gleysolic Static (and Turbic) Cryosols. In the Cryic Great Subgroup of the U.S. Department of Agriculture classification (Soil Survey Staff, 1975), they include Pergelic Cryorthents, Ruptic-Entic Pergelic Cryorthents, Lithic Cryorthents, Ruptic-Entic Lithic

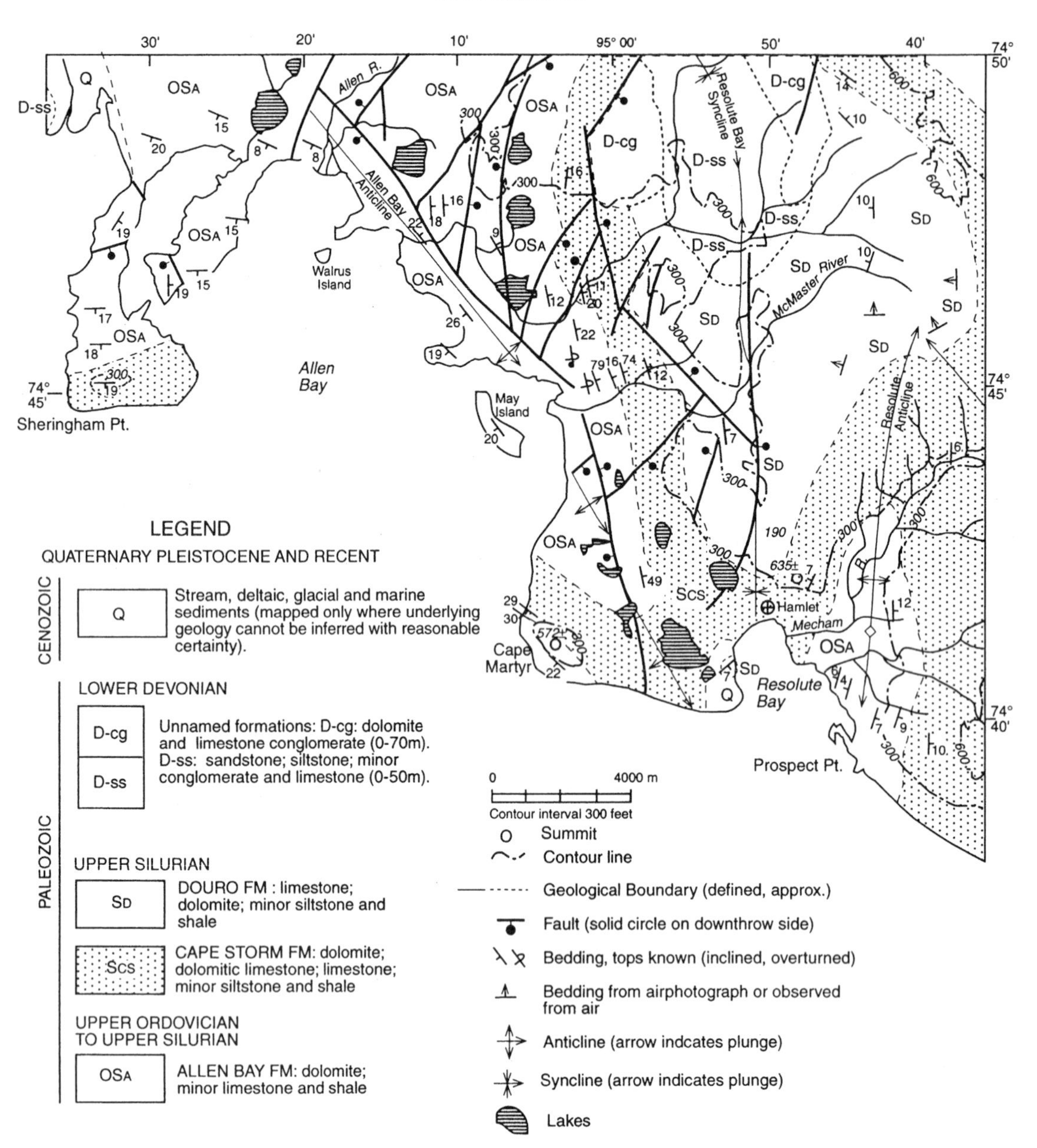

Figure 4. Geologic map of Resolute area and adjacent region, Cornwallis Island, N.W.T. (After Thorsteinsson, 1986; extract.)

Cryorthents, Pergelic Cryaquepts, and Histic Pergelic Cryaquepts (cf. Rieger, 1983, his Table I, p. 210–216; Tarnocai, 1976).

A preliminary study and map of the surficial materials of the Cornwallis Island area and their economic and land-use implications, based on the work of Edlund, D. M. Barnett, and L. A. Dredge, are given by Edlund (1991, p. 20–26).

The vegetation of Cornwallis Island and its relationships to surficial materials are discussed by Edlund (1992). She reported that because of the high alkalinity of the rocks and soils only about 20% of the island is vegetated. Calciferous species dominate, with *Saxifraga oppositifolia* being a major vascular component. Except for Cape Martyr, which is dominated by herbs, the Resolute area is largely a Dryas-Salix barrens dominated by prostrate shrubs and sedges. Moisture regimes determine the dominant communities on both regional and very local scales, the latter being typical of areas immediately downslope from the seasonally retreating edge of perennial snowbanks.

Terminology—patterned ground

Patterned-ground terms used in this report are listed below. Some definitions are quoted from the American Geological Institute *Glossary of Geology* (Bates and Jackson, 1987), cited here as AGI/G. Several terms are from *Glossary of Permafrost and Related Ground-Ice Terms* (Permafrost Subcommittee,

1988), issued by the National Research Council of Canada and cited here as NRCC/G. Other terms are defined for the purpose of this report. Except as otherwise noted all terms are strictly descriptive. "Notes" are mine. Helpful illustrations of patterned-ground terms have been provided by a number of authors, including Cook (1959) and J. Lundqvist (1962).

Circle. "[pat grd] A form of patterned ground whose horizontal mesh is dominantly circular" (AGI/G, p. 119). A variety of such circles occurs (see below).

Debris island. "A *sorted* circle having a diameter of about 1 m and consisting of an isolated patch of finer-textured, compact material surrounded by frost-shattered boulders. . . . Syn: *earth island*; *rubble island*" (AGI/G, p. 170).

Note: Debris islands may correspond to plug S-circles in blocky debris, but detailed published information on the subsurface characteristics of debris islands appears to be largely lacking.

Even-bordered sorted circle (EB S-circle). A sorted circle characterized by a stony border lacking significant relief (≤5 cm) (refer to Figs. 9, 10) as opposed to being ringlike (see "Ring-bordered sorted circle"); the border may be of limited width or part of the general surrounding surface.

Note: This term is introduced here for the purpose of the present report. EB S-circles differ from plug S-circles in not implying subsurface continuity with a plug even though it may exist (see "Plug").

Frost boil (ostiole). "(b) A low mound developed by local differential heaving at a place most favorable for the formation of segregated ice and accompanied by an absence of an insulating cover of vegetation (Taber, 1943, p. 1458–1459)" (AGI/G, p. 261). "A small mound of fresh soil material, formed by *frost action*. A type of nonsorted circle; they are commonly found in fine-grained sediments underlain by permafrost, but also occur in nonpermafrost areas. SYNONYMS: mud boil, stony earth circle" (NRCC/G, p. 34).

Note: Figure 16c cited in NRCC/G, p. 34, shows sorted circles as defined in the AGI/G, p. 628. According to the above list of synonyms, frost boil, ostiole, mud boil, and stony earth circle are formed by frost action, but as noted below, mud boils also involve hydraulic pressures (see "Mud boil").

Mud boil. A nonsorted circle involving " . . . hydraulic pressures and diapiric displacements of water-saturated sediments" (NRCC/G, p. 61).

Note: See "Frost boil" and "Mud circle." Mud boil is not defined in the AGI/G.

Mud circle. "A *nonsorted circle* characterized by a central core of upwardly injected clay, silt, or sometimes fine sand, surrounded by vegetation; the center is round and generally 10 cm to 2 m in diameter. See also: *frost scar; plug [pat grd]*. Syn: *clay boil*; *tundra ostiole*" (AGI/G, p. 436).

Note: Mud circle is not defined in the NRCC/G. According to the above definition of mud circle, clay boil is a synonym. Mud circle was the term used by Mackay (1953) and Cook (1956) for Resolute plug circles (the surface form) as distinct from plugs (the subsurface form). Clay boil, frost boil, and ostiole imply an origin by frost action and are often used synonymously; according to the NRCC/G, mud boil (see above) also involves hydraulic pressure. To preserve a consistent and descriptive terminology, use of clay boil, frost boil, mud boil, and ostiole in the present report is confined to citations from other workers.

Net. "A form of horizontal patterned ground whose mesh is intermediate between a *circle* and a *polygon*" (AGI/G, p. 446).

Note: The adjectives nonsorted and sorted are applicable to nets as well as to circles, polygons, and stripes (cf. AGI/G). Elongate nets on a slope can be transitional to stripes.

Nonsorted circle (N-circle). "A form of patterned ground 'whose mesh is dominantly circular and has a nonsorted appearance due to the absence of a border of stones' (Washburn, 1956, p. 829); developed singly or in groups. Vegetation characteristically outlines the pattern by forming a bordering ridge. When well-developed, it has a distinctive domed central area. Diameter: commonly 0.5 to 3 m. Examples: *mud circle; frost scar; peat ring; tussock ring*" (AGI/G, p. 451).

Note: Many N-circles have risen from depth as revealed by a slight difference in grain size and/or color between the soil of the central area and the surrounding soil (cf. Graf, 1971, p. 128–129). If such evidence is lacking, it may be very difficult to recognize N-circles in barren soil or, if vegetation is present, to distinguish them from strictly surficial forms resulting, for instance, from destruction of the vegetation by needle ice.

Plug. A commonly vertical subsurface cylinder or more irregular mass of more or less cohesive soil, with or without stones, that extends upward from depth and may or may not reach the surface; the surface expression of a plug that breaches the surface is a plug circle or related form of patterned ground (refer to Figs. 7, 13).

Notes: This amended definition is introduced here for the purpose of the present report in place of the definition (AGI/G, p. 512): "*Plug*—(a) A cohesive, commonly vertical column of gravelly material with considerable fines, representing the continuance at depth of a *sorted circle* in a gravel beach, as on Victoria Island, Canada (Washburn, 1956, p. 844). (b) A similar columnlike feature occurring with a *mud circle* (Bird, 1967, p. 194)." Problems are that definition (a) restricts plugs to sorted occurrences on a gravel beach (as opposed to other occurrences) and definition (b) restricts plugs to consisting primarily of fines (see "Mud circle").

Plug as a patterned-ground term was first used by Mackay (1953), who in applying it to Cornwallis Island occurrences used it for subsurface, dominantly vertical, cylindrical forms averaging 20 to 25 cm (8 to 10 in.) that either terminate below the surface or, if reaching it, become a "sorted mud circle" in emerged beach gravel; Mackay also observed plugs in till (Mackay, 1953, p. 31, 35–36). Thus although plugs were strictly subsurface forms, not all plugs were the continuance to depth of a sorted circle. Both "clay plug" and "plug" (with and without quotes) were used by Bunting and Jackson (1970) for plug features on Devon Island. Chambers (1967, p. 20) cited "plugs

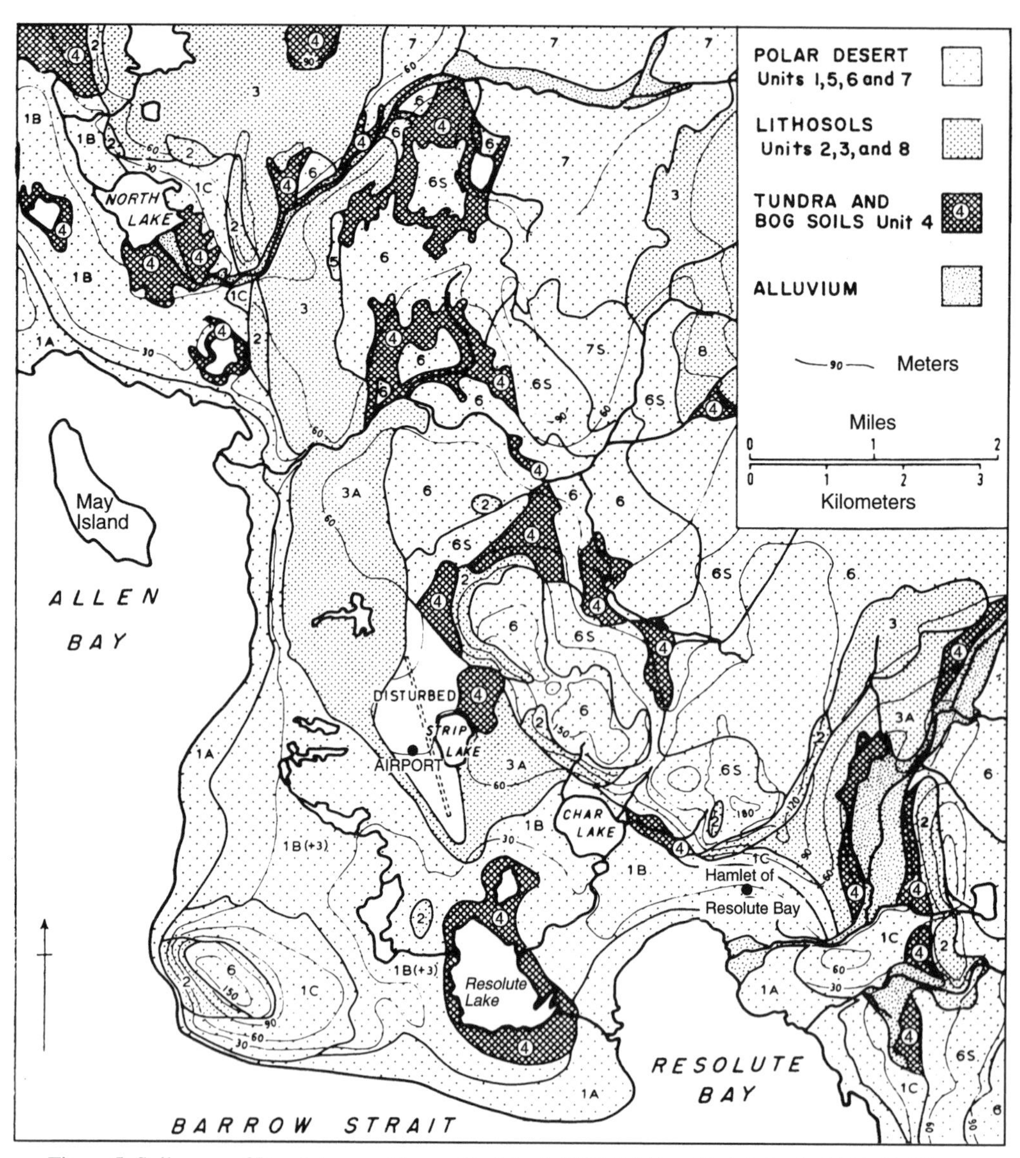

Figure 5. Soils map of Resolute area, Cornwallis Island, N.W.T. (After Cruickshank, 1971, his Fig. 2, p. 199; terrain units after Cruickshank, p. 200, with minor changes); reprinted with permission of the Arctic Institute of North America.

of fines" that break through the surface and form sorted circles at Signy Island in the Subantarctic.

Plugs do not involve what Mackay (1981, p. 1676) called a "plug-like movement" and Egginton and French (1985, p. 1676–1677) described as "pluglike flow," which involved forms quite unlike plugs and an origin by a lateral, downslope displacement process rather than the primarily vertical movement of plugs.

Plug circle. A circular form of patterned ground that is the surface expression of a plug. It includes nonsorted and sorted varieties. See "Plug nonsorted circle," "Plug sorted circle."

Note: This and the following plug terms are introduced for the purpose of the present report; where the context is clear, plug circle or simply circle will sometimes be used for plug S-circle. Most plug circles discussed in the report are the sorted variety. As described later in the section "Transitional Patterned-Ground Forms," plug S-circles may merge with nonsorted forms.

Plug neck. A subsurface, ridgelike soil form connected to a plug, consisting of similar or finer soil and commonly oriented more or less up- and downslope and with lengths measured in centimeters (refer to Fig. 18) (see "Plug ridge").

Plug nonsorted circle (Plug N-circle). A variety of nonsorted circle characterized by being the surface expression of a plug intruding similar textured soil (see "Nonsorted circle").

Note: Plug N-circles, like other N-circles, may be difficult to recognize in the field, since the texture of the central and bordering soils can be very similar; however, differences between the soils are sometimes revealed by slight variations in grain size and/or color.

TERRAIN UNITS

Unit 1: Emerged marine shorelines.

Unit 1A (1): Lowest level, active beach, recent marine deposits, stones angular or subangular, ice-push features, nonsorted material, height range to 3 m (10 to 12 ft) above mean sea-level.

Unit 1A (2): Raised marine features with fresh form, usually with rounded or subangular stones, shelly and fine sand materials, patterned and sorted on level areas, no plants, height range up to 18 m (50 to 60 ft) above mean sea-level.

Unit 1B: Higher marine terrace features, stones of variable roundness, sandy fine material, sorted and patterned ground, sporadic lichen and moss plants, gelifluction modification on slopes, height range 17 to 19 m (50 to 300 ft).

Unit 1C: Raised marine materials and terraces merging with gelifluction material from higher slopes, includes talus and gelifluction material, frost-shattered debris, patterned ground, <5% plant cover, 60 to 120 m (200 to 400 ft) above mean sea-level.

Unit 2: Bedrock outcrop and associated talus slopes; also shattered rock and outcrops on level ground at lower altitude; very few plants.

Unit 3: Rocky, patterned stony ground, level or almost level ground, large rock fragments in large polygons, usually 3 to 4 m (10 to 15 ft) diameter, <10% plant cover.

Unit 3A: Variation of 3 in which fine earth material is present in polygon centers to about 30–40% total, and where polygons tend to be about 1 m (3 ft) in diameter, on level or almost level ground, outlined by large stones. Bedrock outcrop is found in places within 3 and 3A.

Unit 4: Seepage areas with shallow active layer, usually less than 25 cm (10 in). Organic surface horizon Ao 2" or less, and surface colonized by black lichens and mosses. Occurs on sloping sites and frequently develops on gelifluction lobes, and soil stripes. High proportion of material is fine sand size.

Unit 5: Nonsorted patterned- and frost-disturbed ground that has been heaved into hummocks, usually found on gently sloping or level ground, almost no plants.

Unit 6: Silt-clay mantle found generally on elevated level ground, patterned, sometimes frost heaved and contains small limestone chips, weakly sorted or nonsorted. 6S is the very stony phase. Few plants present in either.

Unit 7: Red sandy dolomite material—similar to unit 6 in texture, but appears to be a little more sandy (usually about 70 to 80% sand in fine earth) and contains fewer stones—patterned and frost disturbed, but only weakly sorted. Polygons were not a feature of units 6 or 7. 7S is the very stony phase. About 50% cover of lichens and mosses gives the unit a distinctive appearance.

Unit 8: Shattered limestone—broken into fragments 10 to 25 cm (4 to 10 in) in diameter—patterned but only weakly sorted. Occurs on level or nearly level ground. Very few plants present.

Plug pit. A more or less conical ground-surface depression, commonly 5 to 15 cm deep (but up to 30 cm deep, Mackay, 1953, p. 35), underlain by a plug.

Plug ridge. A subsurface, primarily linear form, commonly more or less parallel to a contour, similar to a plug in constitution but with lengths measured in meters, from which individual plugs (with any associated plug circles) may arise as pinnacles (refer to Fig. 14). Plug ridges are commonly associated with plug rows.

Plug row. A row of more or less closely spaced plugs and any associated plug circles or semicircles, aligned more or less parallel to a contour, especially at a decrease in slope; rows may be multiple and closely spaced and join or diverge slightly from the contour and each other (refer to Figs. 14, 27, 30) (see "Plug ridge").

Plug sorted circle (Plug S-circle). A plug circle characterized by a stony border that is commonly but not necessarily part of the general surrounding surface (refer to Fig. 19).

Plug sorted semicircle (Plug S-semicircle). A slope form of patterned ground characterized by a plug whose upslope half has a low but abrupt side that, with respect to upslope soil, forms an arcuate, convex-upslope stony border and a semicircular pattern; the downslope side of the semicircle is characterized by a relatively even surface of fines or stony fines trailing off downslope (refer to Figs. 24 through 27, 29, 30).

Notes: A plug S-semicircle may be similar or perhaps identical to an "upslope polygon," a term used by Rudberg (1969, p. 147; his Fig. 7, p. 149), and by Egginton (1972, p. 1, 42), who also referred to them as hummocks. However, "polygon" seems inappropriate, "upslope" is ambiguous in implying the location of the form itself as opposed to the presence of an upslope side, and "hummock" is commonly applied to different forms.

Patterns along the inner edge of hillside benches on the steep slopes above PE 83-3 (see the section "Occurrences in Miscellaneous Deposits") were surficially somewhat similar to plug S-semicircles, but excavation did not reveal any underlying plugs. Rather, the pattern may have been associated with slumping. The benches are of uncertain origin, but in one excavation what was probably a small ice wedge was partially exposed at the inner edge, although at an angle of some 55° to it. Other possibly important factors are structural control and perhaps ice-marginal drainage.

Polygon. "A form of horizontal patterned ground whose mesh is tetragonal, pentagonal, or hexagonal. . . ." (AGI/G, p. 518).

Note: The adjectives nonsorted and sorted are applicable, as with circles, nets, and stripes (cf. AGI/G, p. 518). Some polygons can occur on slopes but most deform to nets and stripes on a slope.

Ring-bordered sorted circle (RB S-circle). A variety of sorted circle characterized by a ringlike stony border having a relief exceeding 5 cm; the circle is not necessarily continuous with a plug at depth. In the Resolute area, stony borders are up to some 10 cm high (refer to Fig. 54) (see "Sorted circle").

Note: This variety of sorted circle, introduced here for the purpose of the present report, is exemplified by the classical variety made famous by participants in the 1910 Spitsbergen field excursion of the 11th International Geological Congress (cf. Salomon, 1910; Högbom, 1914, p. 257–319; Meinardus, 1912a, b; and Miethe, 1912, among others) and by a host of subsequent workers.

Sorted circle (S-circle). "A form of *patterned ground* 'whose mesh is dominantly circular and has a sorted appearance commonly due to a border of stones surrounding finer material' (Washburn, 1956, p. 827); developed singly or in groups. Diameter: a few centimeters to more than 10 m; the stone border may be 35 cm high and 8 to 12 cm wide. . . . Syn: *stone circle; stone ring; stone wreath; rock wreath; frost circle*" (AGI/G, p. 628-629).

Note: Of the above synonyms, the first two are the more common. As used here, there are several varieties of S-circle (see "Debris island," "Even-bordered sorted circle," "Plug sorted circle," "Ring-bordered sorted circle").

Stripes. A form of patterned ground occurring on slopes and characterized by parallel lines of fines-rich soil (with or without stones), commonly alternating with lines of stones or vegetation oriented along the fall line.

Note: This is an abbreviated definition introduced for the purpose of the present report. The adjectives nonsorted and sorted are applicable, as with circles, nets, and polygons.

Terminology—soils

General. Grain-size analyses in this report are given by dry weight according to the Wentworth grade scale (modified) unless otherwise indicated. Especially in the case of a diamicton (see below), this usage (Tables 1 through 16) lends itself to a terminology indicative of percent by weight of each grade size present in (1) the specimen as a whole (Washburn et al., 1963), (2) truncated, and (3) in the matrix only (see "Nontruncated analyses," "Truncated analyses").

The Casagrande (1931, p. 169) criterion of 3 to 10% content of fines smaller than 0.02 mm in diameter (within silt range), depending on the uniformity of the soil, has been an often-quoted rule of thumb for determining the susceptibility of soils to frost heaving. However, as frequently reviewed (cf. Washburn, 1979, p. 68–70), this criterion is also influenced by other factors, and the subject as a whole is complex. In general, however, plugs in the Resolute area commonly have a fines content of 10% or more and would tend to be distinctly frost susceptible if water saturated.

The following soil terms are used as shown below, unless in some quotations or as otherwise indicated.

Diamicton. ". . . Any nonsorted or poorly sorted terrigeneous sediment that consists of sand and/or larger particles in a muddy matrix" (Flint et al., 1960a, p. 509; 1960b; see "Terminology—soils, General" above).

Note: The sediment of many plugs in the Resolute area is a diamicton, as is also true of many other soils in the region.

Diapirism. As loosely applied to soils, diapirism is a genetic term commonly implying surfaceward soil movement resulting from differential frost heaving and/or from lower bulk densities at depth than higher in the soil profile. The cause of surfaceward movement and whether the movement is observed, inferred, or assumed should be specified if possible.

Note: In the apparent absence of a formal definition of soil diapirism, the one above has been tentatively adopted by the author and Bernard Hallet, one of his colleagues at the University of Washington.

Fines. Grain sizes (clay and silt) less than 0.062 mm in diameter as defined in the Wentworth grade scale.

Gravel. Grain sizes exceeding 2 mm in diameter as defined in the Wentworth grade scale, thus including granule, pebble, and cobble sizes and boulders if rounded or blocks if angular (cf. AGI/G, p. 287).

Note: Boulders or large cobbles were rarely present in the areas where soil specimens were collected. Although noted, they would have been omitted from grain-size analyses as being unrepresentative.

Nontruncated analyses. Grain-size analyses of specimens whose upper grain-size limit is not capped. A number of the specimens collected were too small to be statistically reliable, yet nevertheless indicated prevalent grain sizes (see "Truncated analyses").

Openwork gravel. "Said of a gravel with unfilled voids" (AGI/G, p. 462).

Note: Openwork gravel (including beach gravel) may have an appreciable content of fines adhering to the gravel or incompletely filling voids in it.

Soil. "All unconsolidated materials above bedrock" (AGI/G, p. 264).

Truncated analyses. Grain-size analyses whose upper grain-size limit is capped to provide statistically more reliable comparative data than in the case of specimens whose analysis may be skewed by the presence of stone(s) in soil specimens too small to be statistically reliable (see "Nontruncated analyses").

EARLIER OBSERVATIONS

Nichols (1953, p. 275) described plug circles he observed in the Resolute area in 1948 as follows:

Frost mounds are very common in the swales of the elevated beaches. They are from 1 to more than 3 feet in diameter and are several inches high. Roundstones and fine material are found on their surfaces and they are surrounded by angular fragments usually without interstitial fines. Shells are more common on them than on the surrounding terrain because they are in general composed of finer material. The presence of the roundstones unmodified by solution or frost action proves that the mounds are now being formed. That they have been formed recently is also shown by the fact that some of them rest on a thin soil which had earlier been developed on the beach gravels.[5]

Mackay (1953) devoted a brief but perceptive paper to Resolute polygons, plugs, plug S-circles, and their associa-

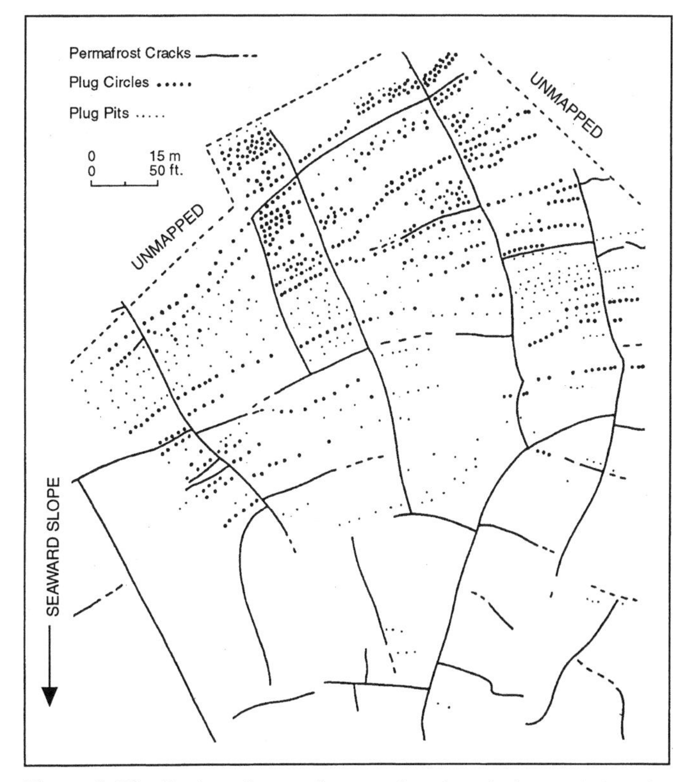

Figure 6. Distribution of permafrost cracks, plug circles, and plug pits in emerged beach gravel along the shore of Resolute Bay. (After Mackay, 1953, his Fig. 3, p. 34, but term "mud" omitted to accord with present text.)

tion with emerged beaches (Fig. 6). His observations on plugs (Mackay, p. 35) showed that in many places the plug forms parallel contours and that beginning within 6 to 9 m (20 to 30 ft) of the shore of Resolute Bay, plugs in the beach gravel underlie conical pits (plug pits) several centimeters (inches) to 30 cm (1 ft) deep. The plugs were 10 to 15 cm (4 to 6 in.) in diameter, and in summer some oozed water when broken open. They commenced at a depth of 50 to 64 cm (20 to 25 in.), with some plugs resting on ice lenses 30 cm (1 ft) or more thick and 90 cm (3 ft) or more in diameter (Fig. 7). The ice contained a few stones and waferlike fragments of clay. With increasing altitude and age of beaches, the pits became fewer and were replaced by "mud circles" (plug circles), 20 to 25 cm (8 to 10 in.) in diameter, which were the manifestation of plugs that had reached the surface. Some circles could be slightly convex and extend 2.5 cm (1 in.) above the beach surface.

Mackay (1953, p. 36) also made the stimulating observation, discussed later, that "As more and more plugs reach the surface, they begin to coalesce. . . . Individual plugs may eventually lose their identities as they merge to form other types of patterned ground." Subsequently Mackay (1983, p. 130) commented that summer ice lensing might account for the upward movement of plugs. Mackay's 1953 description makes clear that plugs were formerly widespread and well developed in the

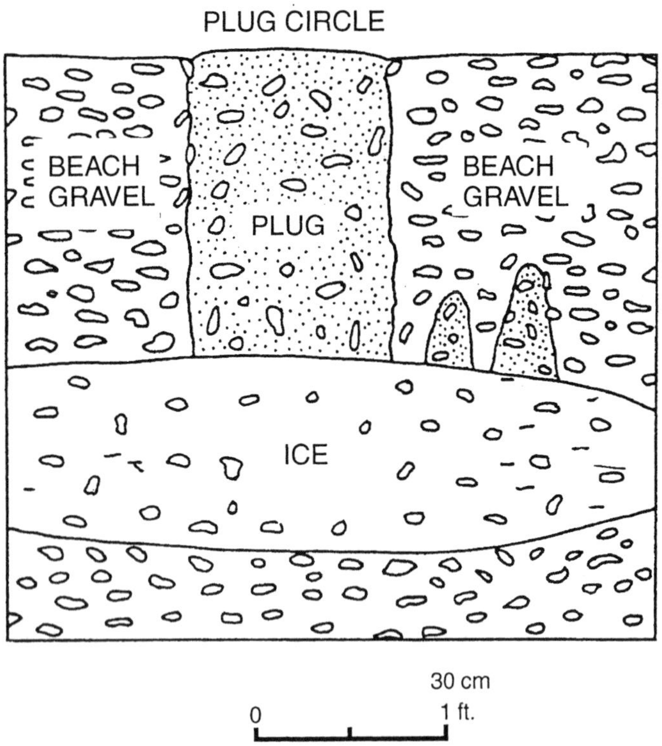

Figure 7. Cross section of well-developed plug and two satellite plugs overlying ice lens; plug circle at surface. (After Mackay, 1953, his Fig. 4, p. 34, but term "mud" omitted to accord with present text.)

immediate vicinity of Resolute Bay. However, extensive bulldozing there has now disrupted many occurrences.

Cook carried out a series of valuable geomorphic studies in the Resolute area, including soil-temperature observations during freezing of the active layer (Cook, 1955) and other observations on plugs and associated "mud circles" (plug S-circles) (Cook, 1956). He observed that in places the circles were aligned on the downslope side of permafrost cracks and could also occur around and within permafrost-crack junctions. The average diameter of 400 circles was 38 cm (15 in.). He found that flat stones tended to lie flat against plug sides, that plugs (six to seven measured) averaged 73% fines by volume and 56.5%[6] by weight (with maximum departure of 5%), and that per unit volume many more stones surrounded plugs than occurred within them. In addition, Cook (1956, p. 16–17) found that plug circles in areas that had been scraped and smoothed by bulldozing to the extent that the circles were unrecognizable began to reappear within a week and ooze milky water containing suspended clay. Dye put in the base of a plug that had been exhumed by removing the surrounding gravel rose to the top of the plug within a month, apparently by evaporation and a wick-like action. He concluded that plugs may be injection phenomena due to the pressure generated by a freezing front advancing laterally from the coarser-grained soil encircling a plug, whose freezing would tend to be delayed by its finer grain size and higher water retention compared to the gravel.

Egginton (1972) excavated a number of plugs and conducted granulometric and dye studies. He reported that more fines (silt and clay) occur on the upslope than downslope side of plug circles and furthermore that the borders had more fines at the base than the top—a situation he attributed to downward seepage of fines from higher in the profile (Egginton, 1972, p. 56).

In comparing the granulometry of plug S-semicircles ("upslope polygons" and "hummocks" in his terminology) with other "polygons" (presumably plug S-circles) and small and large forms of each, Egginton found little difference between them. In addition, he observed that a subsurface ridge of fines (probably a plug neck; see the section "Terminology—patterned ground") joined some nearby "polygons." Furthermore, he found forms that he believed to be developing "polygons" that disturbed the surface, and excavation revealed underlying plugs as described by Mackay (Egginton, 1972, p. 63–64).

Egginton carried out a series of dye experiments, injecting rhodamine into and adjacent to patterned-ground features. He found that dye injected into the base of fines rose toward the surface and near there propagated radially and toward coarse borders. When introduced into borders, it followed them around the central areas. Finally, with respect to genesis of the patterned-ground forms, he suggested that soil may follow a similar circulatory pattern (Egginton, 1972, p. 101–102). In considering the influence of slope on features, he reported that "polygons" and stripes occurred on gradients of 0° to 2° and 2° to 5°, respectively, hummocks on gradients of 3° to 12°, and mudflows and solifluction lobes on gradients of 14° (Egginton, 1972, p. 113). A number of Egginton's observations were remarkably on target for having been made during a single field season as part of an undergraduate program.

Bunting and Jackson (1970) examined a plug they excavated at Radstock Bay, Devon Island, east of Cornwallis Island. The plug was in beach material derived from cherty shales and dolomitic limestones overlying a presumed till, which was "permafrosted" at a depth of 48 to 55 cm (late August 1969). The plug soil, derived from the presumed till, intruded generally angular and slabby beach debris, which was patterned in circular fashion above the plug. The surface form, although circular, was termed a polygon. The plug (Sp. 7) itself at a depth of 15 to 25 cm consisted of " . . . a gravelly sandy clay loam with a distinct bimodal particle size distribution. The organic matter content is remarkably low [0.7%]." At a depth of 25 to 30 cm, the soil (Sp. 9) was " . . . a gravelly clay loam with a significantly higher organic matter content [4.1%], low bulk density [1.46] and a high content of rounded fine to medium gravel in a ground mass of low liquid limit [33.8]" (Bunting and Jackson, 1970, p. 202–203).

Their Tables 1 and 2 show that gravel dominated in the plug (Bunting and Jackson, 1970, their Tables 1 and 2, p. 202), and they reported (p. 205) that "The upper part of the clay plug has significantly higher clay contents than the lower parts. . . . " However, this difference in the upper part of the plug was only 4.4% as calculated from their Table 1; if recalculated for the matrix only (total sand, silt, and clay of the plug) as in their

Table 2, the higher clay percent (4.9%) was in the lower part of the plug. In either case the difference between the upper and lower parts was small. To facilitate comparison with several nontruncated Resolute grain-size analyses, the plug data from their Tables 1 and 2 (excluding a 5-cm interval from a different plug) are rounded, rearranged, and summarized in Table 1 of my report. The Radstock Bay plug is uniformly higher in fines (clay + silt) and lower in gravel than nontruncated Resolute comparisons provided by PE 90-1 and PE 90-2 (Table 4) and by PE 95-1, PE 95-2, and PE 95-3 (refer to Figs. 32, 33, 35; Tables 7, 9, 11).

On the basis of their detailed granulometric study, Bunting and Jackson (1970, abs., p. 194) advanced the hypothesis "... that some polygonal features must result from the interaction of two layers of material of differing texture, rather than through differential sorting of stones and fines derived from a heterogeneous parent material." With many plug circles, this is clearly the case, as discussed later in my report. Among other observations, Bunting and Jackson reported that the plug had a higher liquid limit and lower bulk density than the surrounding gravel, that it had an isolated pocket of high organic content, and that depth to the "permafrosted" horizon was 5 to 8 cm deeper in the plug than in the surrounding gravel. Their report is an exceptionally detailed analysis of a plug.

OCCURRENCES IN EMERGED BEACH GRAVEL

Experimental site C (ES C)

ES C was in an area of plug S-circles in otherwise undisturbed beach gravel between McMaster River on the north and the east-west section of the road to the present beach on the south (Fig. 3). The site was mapped to show the distribution of the circles and other features (Fig. 8). At 14 m south of the north end of the map, the gradient in the upper part above the 70-cm contour averaged above 4°, and below this, about 7° (to the closest degree).

In addition to a number of excavations, ES C included a heave frame to measure frost heaving and settling of two adjacent circles and surrounding gravel (Figs. 9, 10). The frame comprised two lines of aluminum rods that were positioned through the frame bars and that rested on pads in contact with the soil surface. The bars were anchored to steel corner posts punched to refusal in the gravel with a Pionjar gasoline-powered jackhammer on 1 August 1985. The northeast and southeast posts extended to depths of 108.5 and 113.5 cm, respectively, the western anchor post to 75.4 cm. The greater depths were probably in an ice wedge underlying the gravel. All three posts were in permafrost when installed. The frost-table depth on 4 August in the center of 10 nearby circles averaged 57 cm, ranging from 49 to 61 cm; the depth in adjacent gravel averaged 44 cm, ranging from 36 to 55 cm. Frost-table depths later in the season in subsequent years were not significantly different except perhaps for the warm summers of 1987 and 1988 when new excavations in the area were lacking, but frost-table depths were unlikely to have approached the insertion depths. Frequent level checks of the bars to ±10 min of arc also indicated end-post stability throughout the observation period.

The heave-frame record (Figs. 11A–11D, 12A–12D) extends to September 1990 but is discontinuous, since some of the rods had to be replaced because of disturbance (foxes?). This discontinuity and the lack of a detailed initial map of the plug circles inhibited establishment of an absolute record, but the heaving and settling relative to the initial topography as shown in the continuous segments of the record are estimated to be accurate to ± 2 mm.

The record clearly shows the expectable correlation between heaving and settling of plug circles with the weather conditions recorded at Resolute A, the airfield weather station 4 km to the southeast, and shown for the period of interest in the temperature and precipitation graphs accompanying the heaving and settling curves in Figures 11A–11D and 12A–12D.

The uninterrupted record of heaving and settling along the northeast bar, summed over the 5-yr period from 18 August 1985 to 18 August 1990 (Figs. 11A–11D), ranged from –5 mm at rod 16 on relatively fine gravel to –41 mm at rod 4 on intermediate gravel. However, all the rods on the fines-rich gravel of the northeast plug circle had interrupted records. For the southeast bar and the same observation dates (Figs. 12A–12D), the record ranged from –2 mm at rod 3 on intermediate gravel to –35 mm at rod 9 on fines-rich gravel of the southeast plug circle. Rod 14 of the southeast bar, the only rod on coarse gravel at either bar, registered –10 mm. Not surprisingly, the curves as a whole demonstrate that the plug circles generally showed the most heaving and settling, although rods 1 through 5 of the northeast bar exhibited a similar behavior, perhaps reflecting underlying fines-rich gravel. Precipitation during the May–September period does not appear to have had a significant effect on the curves.

Overall there was a lowering of the soil surface during the 5-yr observation period. The heave-frame records show that this lowering was due primarily to the July-August mean air temperatures. Their sum (Thawing Index) of 251.8 in 1987 and 286.9 in 1988 as calculated from Resolute A station records was the highest for these months, not only for the 1985–1990 period but also for the preceding 5 yr. The generally close correlation of frost heaving and thaw settling at ES C with these records is apparent in Figures 11A–11D and 12A–12D. Thaw settling did not normally occur unless Resolute daily minima were warmer than –2 °C and maxima approached their highest values. Heaving, which became noticeable by mid-August, was generally associated with Resolute minima of –2 °C or colder. Possibly a significant part of the heaving was by upward freezing from the permafrost table, judging from probing and excavations to the frost table in the area at various times and locations. By mid-September, freeze-up was well underway, with daily maxima as well as minima being consistently below 0 °C and dropping.

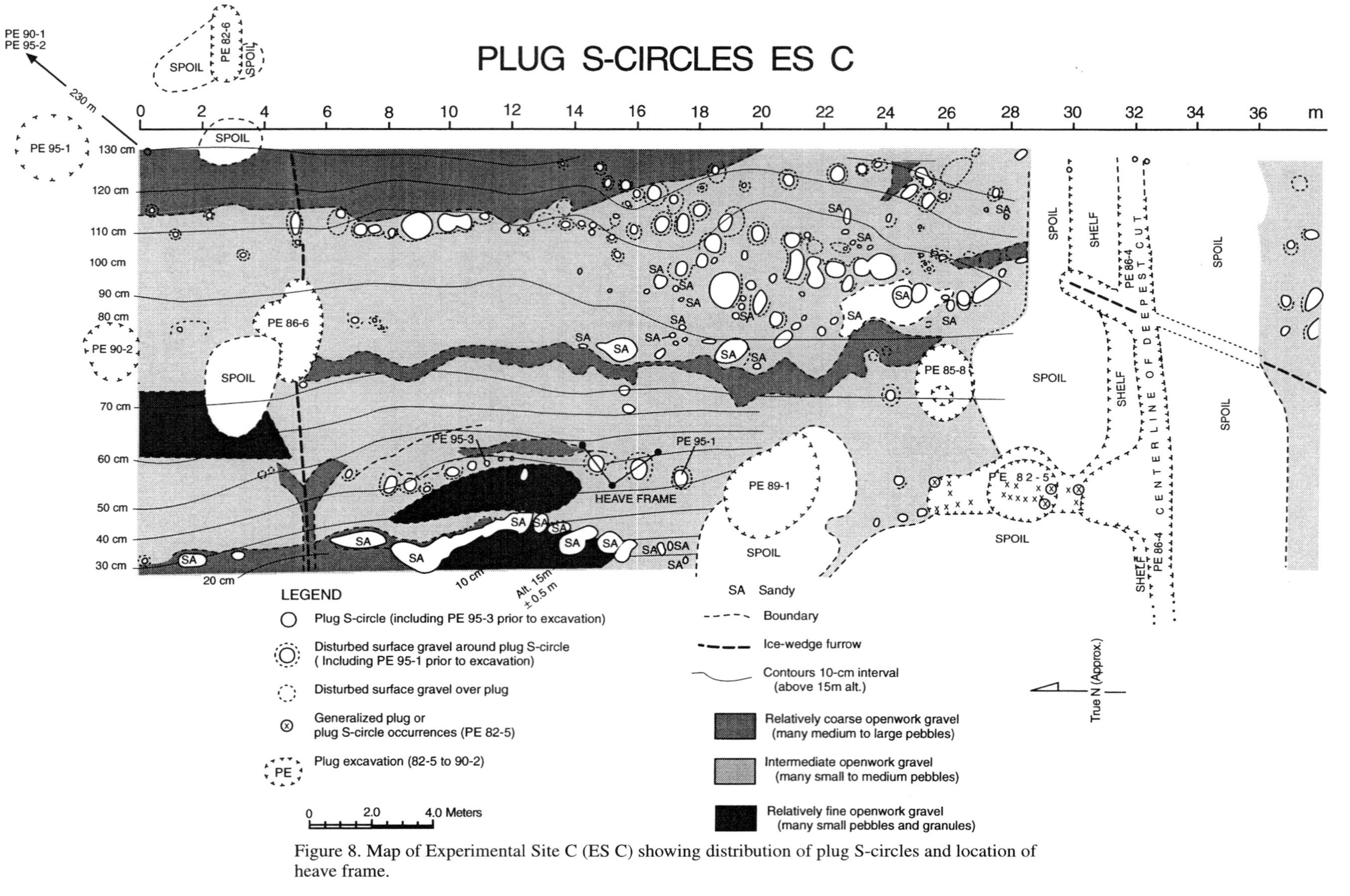

Figure 8. Map of Experimental Site C (ES C) showing distribution of plug S-circles and location of heave frame.

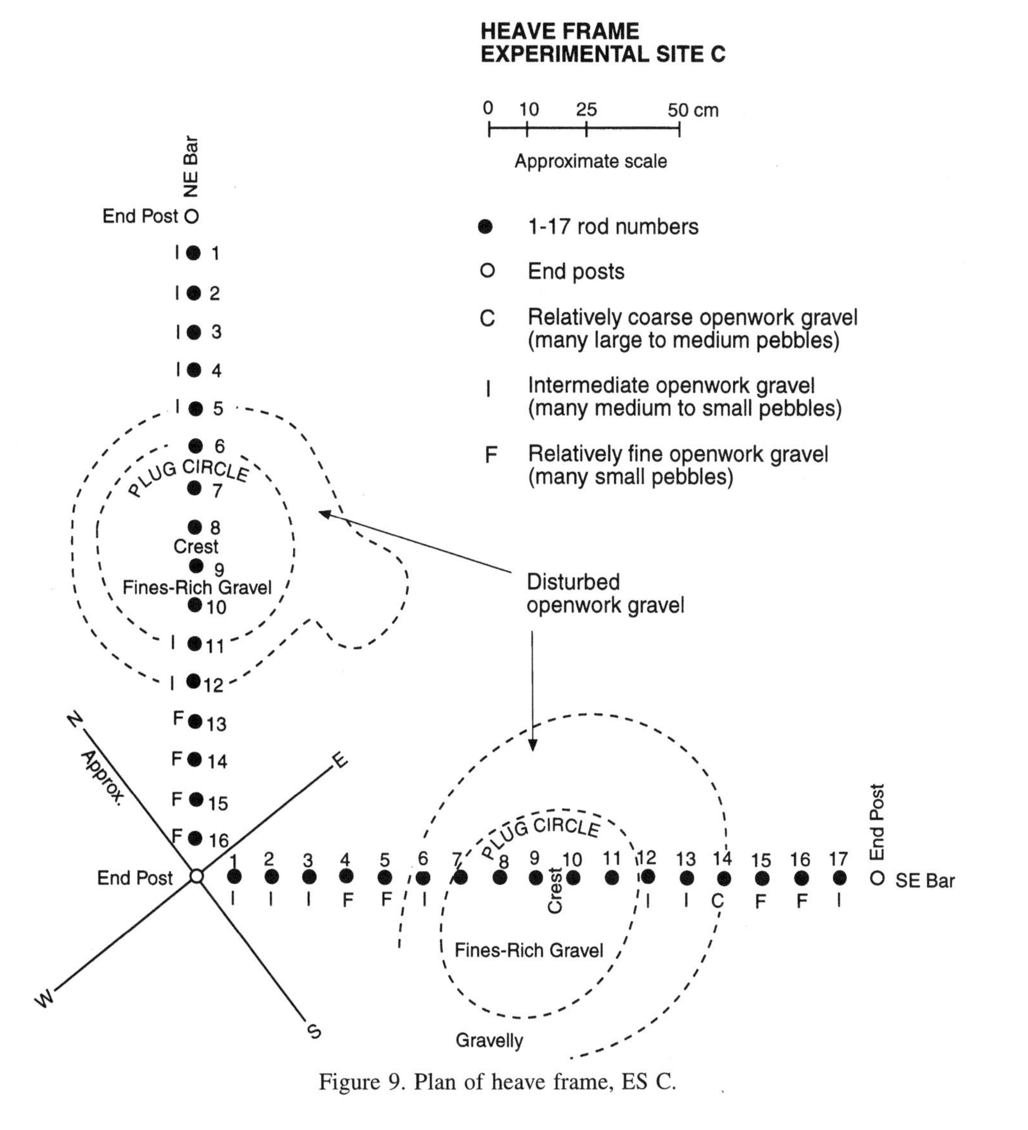

Figure 9. Plan of heave frame, ES C.

Excavations

A number of plug excavations (PE) were carried out on emerged beaches during the present study. They confirm many of the earlier observations and add further information. ES C was one of the principal areas investigated (Figs. 3, 8). Here as elsewhere difficulty of excavating in frozen ground and the accumulation of thaw water in depressions often complicated observations.

The lowest altitude at which plug circles were observed in the Resolute area was 2.5 to 3.0 m near the south side of the road south of ES C. (Some nearby circles 1 to 2 m lower were associated with geliflucting debris of an undercut beach.) The in-situ circles constituted a complex of small contiguous circles that seemed about to amalgamate.

PE 82-5. Plug excavation 82-5 was in undisturbed beach gravel at an altitude of about 15 m, 10 m south of the ES C heave frame (Fig. 8). The plug S-circles in the area tended to be aligned along the contour parallel to decreases in gradient, but pronounced

Figure 10. Heave frame, ES C. Southeast bar in foreground. Rods are 10 cm apart.

beach ridges were absent. The gravel of the plugs was dominantly rounded, whereas the surface gravel surrounding the plug circles was comparatively angular. Shell fragments were common in the circles but less so in the surrounding gravel.

PE 82-5 was started along a plug row of S-circles parallel to the contour. The first of the circles and associated plugs excavated in beach gravel consisted of a cohesive diamicton of fines-rich gravel, surrounded by loose openwork gravel. The surrounding gravel was scooped out to the frost table (depth 39 cm, 11 July 1982), leaving the plug standing in relief (Fig. 13). The excavation continued parallel to the contour and exposed below the surface a plug ridge (Fig. 14) consisting

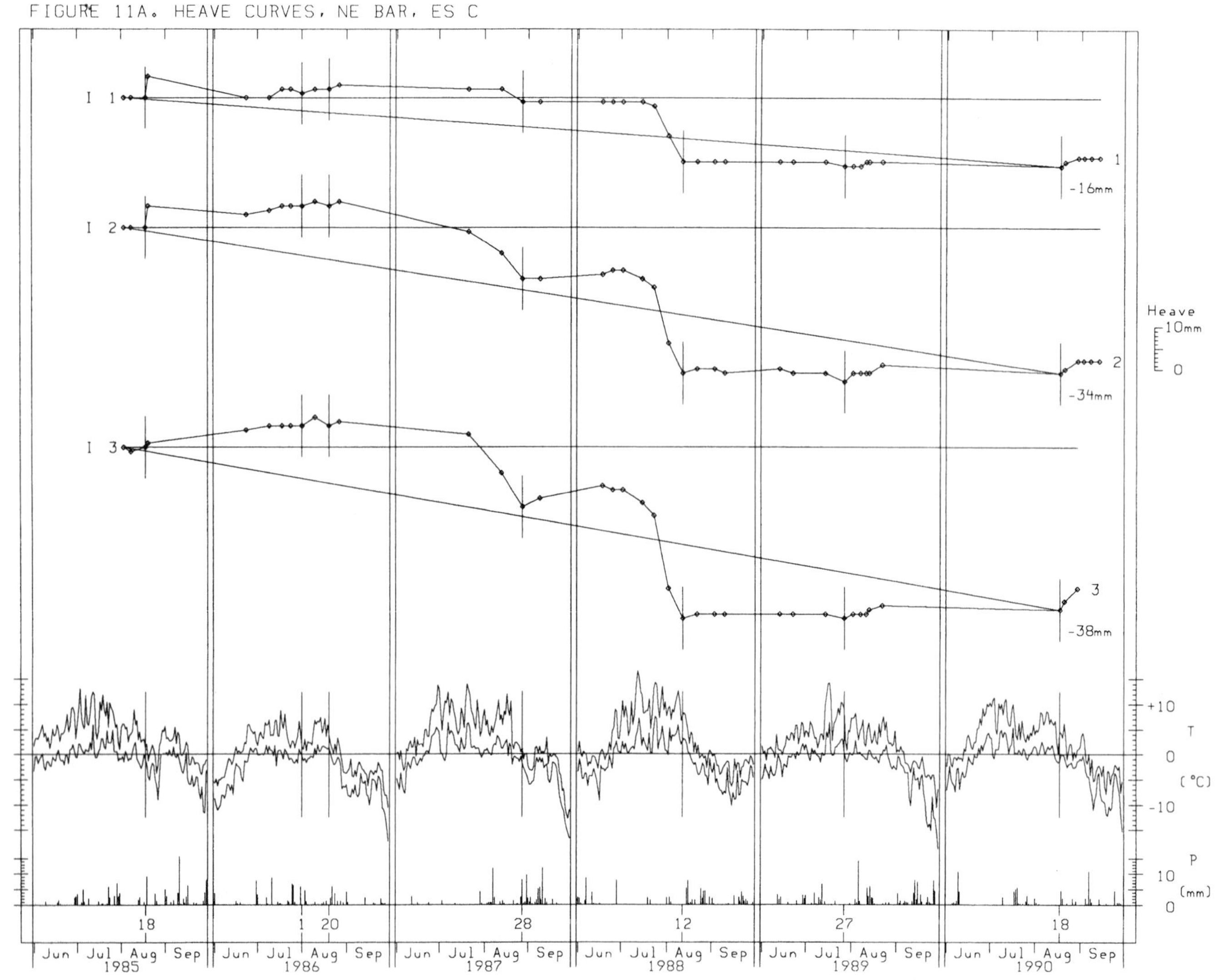

Figures 11A–D (on this and following three pages). Graphs of heaving and settling of ground surface below northeast bar of heave frame, ES C. Heaving and settling of the ground below the northeast and southeast bars of the heave frame were measured by changes in height of rods that extended through each bar and rested on the ground; each rod had a foot pad that prevented a rod from penetrating soft soil. Changes in rod height were relative to the existing topography when the rods were installed; that is, the low, domelike plug circles and the comparatively even surface of the surrounding gravel (Figs. 9, 10). An absolute record was inhibited as explained in the text. Letters C, I, F, and FR indicate coarse, intermediate, fine, and fines-rich gravel, respectively. The (horizontal) time axis is discontinuous. One linear scale is used for June through September. During this period, abrupt changes in the heave curves are shown by long vertical ticks corresponding to the dates indicated in the temperature (max-min T °C) and precipitation (P, mm) record at Resolute A at the airfield. The graphed weather data were constructed from the daily weather records for Resolute A, but the records themselves were eliminated to conserve space. Appendix A, Table 1, is a long-term summary only. A highly compressed scale is used for the period from October through May of the following year. Each reading is indicated by a square dot, the dots being connected by line segments as a visual aid. The horizontal line is the zero reference value for changes subsequent to installation of the heave frame in 1985. The dot enclosed in a large diamond indicates a record interruption due to rod replacement following the last reading of a year and the first reading of the next year. Since the ordinate of the curve during the interruption is unknown, the curve is arbitrarily rescaled to the 1985 zero reference value. Both the latter and the line connecting the dots are labeled by rod number.

(Sp. 82-9-8A, truncated at 8 mm) of a nonplastic, clayey$_3$-sandy$_{19}$ silt$_{38}$-gravel$_{40}$ of the same diamicton as the exhumed plug and connecting it to three other plugs rising from the ridge as pinnacles, one of which reached the surface as a plug S-circle. Additional plugs were exhumed slightly downslope from the ridge, and further removal of gravel from around several plugs that reached the surface showed they had a subsurface relief of at least 40 cm at the frost-table depth on 8 September 1982, a depth probably reflecting some upward freezing from the permafrost table, judging from the rapidly lowering air temperatures during this time of year.

Some circles were quite separate from each other; others were contiguous, resulting in a more or less linear, upslope-facing relief with convex-upslope elements (Fig. 14). The overall pattern was transitional to that of plug S-semicircles (see the section "Terminology—patterned ground") but less pronounced and regular and with less downslope extension, presumably due to the low (ca. 3 to 6°) gradient of ES C. The slight upslope depressions were much less prominent than the occasional, much less common permafrost cracks that also tended to parallel the contour as well as running transversely. Except for the obvious permafrost cracks that had some isolated plug S-circles along them, excavation failed to reveal a confirmed subsurface crack conforming to the linear pattern of closely spaced plug circles. However, as discussed later in connection with PE 86-4, excavation there did reveal a plug sitting on an ice wedge where a crack was fading into a probable plug ridge. The possibility that such ridges may have been initiated along old and now fossil permafrost cracks is not eliminated but seems doubtful because the spacing between parallel sets of plug circles rising from plug ridges is much closer than that between recognized permafrost cracks in the Resolute area (cf. Fig. 6) or elsewhere in my experience.

The excavation was continued in 1986 and 1987 and eventually became about 5 m long and 2 m wide. It confirmed that the circular appearance of a number of plug S-circles here represented pinnacles along plug ridges. Overall the excavation exposed four plug ridges whose main trend was parallel to the strandlines but had subsidiary trends at a slight angle, giving rise to a number of pinnacles, some of which reached the sur-

FIGURE 11B. HEAVE CURVES, NE BAR, ES C

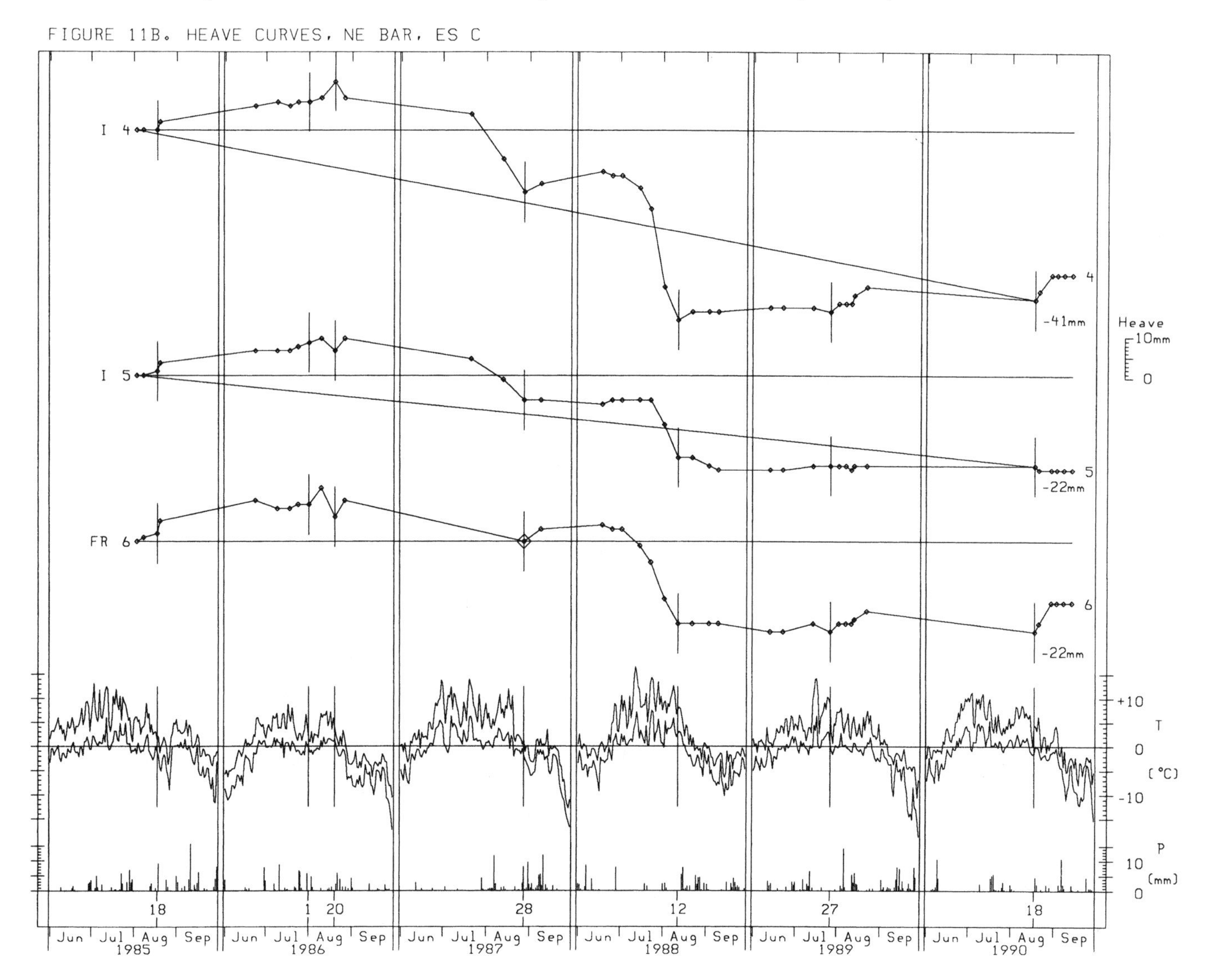

face as plug S-circles (Figs. 15, 16A–16B). Plugs were of variable size and shape, and several of the more prominent ones leaned slightly downslope.

The most prominent plug ridge with its pinnacles was transected in 1986 to the then frost table at a depth of about 60 cm from the original 1982 surface and was continued in 1987 to a depth of about 125 cm. Consecutive plug cross sections southward in 1986 and 1987 with co-linear cross sections northward from PE 86-4 (Fig. 8) showed that the plugs consisted of a compact clayey-silty-gravel dominated by rounded pebbles usually in contact with each other and that the fines were primarily interstitial rather than occurring as a matrix around isolated stones. Openwork gravel with sizable shell fragments was exposed below the main plug ridge at a depth of some 50 cm below the original 1982 surface—a depth probably near the permafrost table in that year. The openwork gravel dipped downslope, and interstices in frozen openwork gravel at greater depth were ice filled (6 August 1986). Silty gravel appeared below the openwork gravel at a depth of about 65 cm upon further thawing (Figs. 17A–17B). Overall the cross sections revealed a stratigraphy of openwork gravel overlying thinner, alternating or intertonguing beds of sand, openwork gravel, silty gravel, and clayey silty gravel, the last commonly compact and similar to the plug soil. Bedding was commonly even except where beds pinched out or were distorted by plugs. The thaw depth in the fines-rich gravel was 2 to 3 cm deeper than in the openwork gravel. Probably the thawed openwork gravel below many of the plugs had underlain the original 1982 permafrost table and was formerly ice rich. Excavation of PE 85-8, which revealed ice-rich gravel at a depth of 39 cm (9 August 1985) 3 m upslope from PE 82-5, supports this interpretation. However, the thawed openwork gravel below at least one of the excavated plugs at PE 82-5 did not continue upslope as a clearly defined horizon but appeared to merge with a diamicton.

PE 82-6. Not all plugs and plug S-circles at ES C (Fig. 8) paralleled the contour; some trended up- and downslope, especially alongside permafrost cracks. Others, as at PE 82-6, were isolated plug circles. The plug of PE 82-6 rested on an ice lens

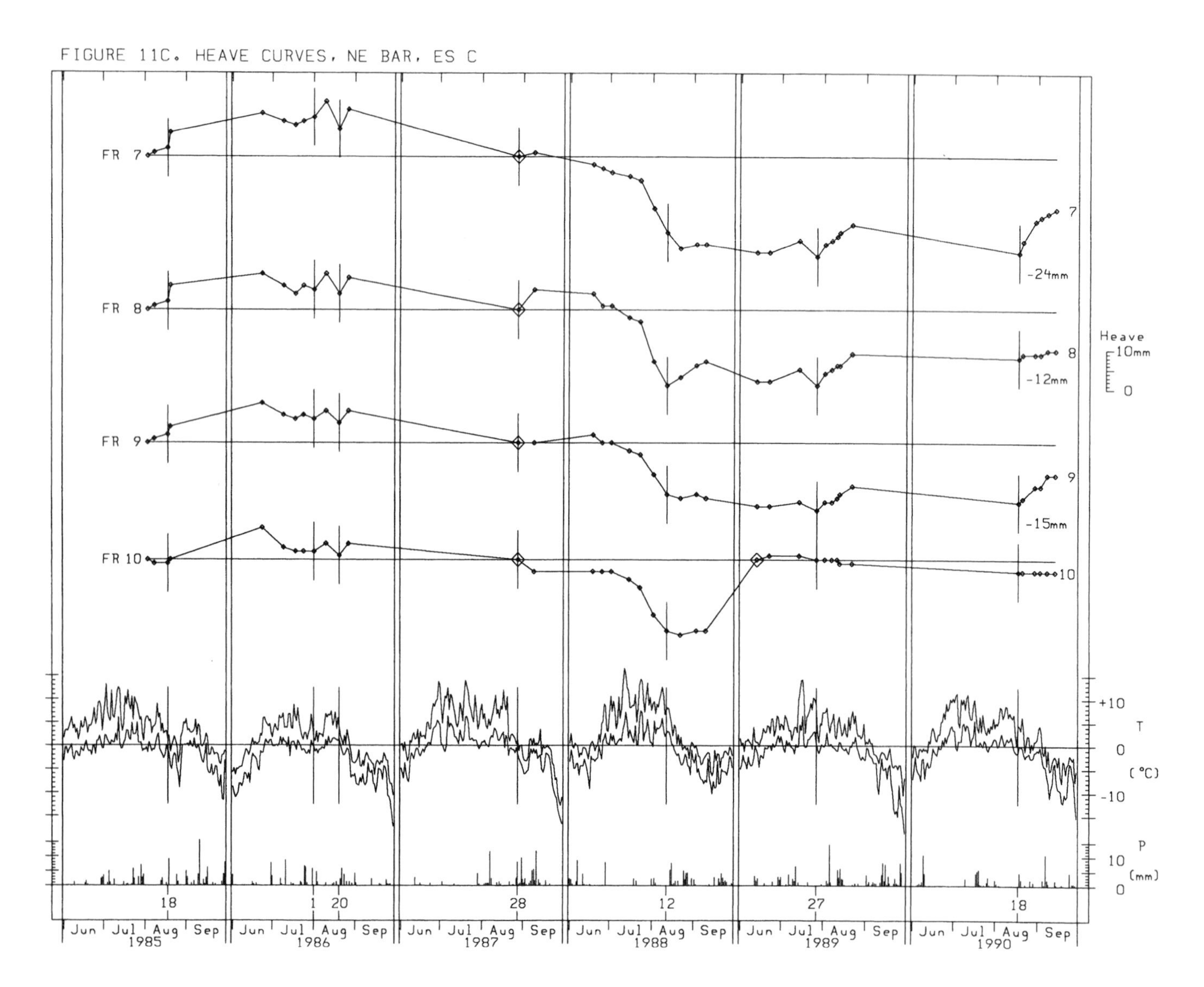

1.5 cm thick, whereas the adjacent beach gravel contained mainly interstitial ice. The plug thawed to a depth of about 45 cm and 2 to 3 cm less in the adjacent gravel (20 July 1982). Rising from the frost table at the plug and of similar composition was an upslope plug neck with a relief up to 12 cm (Fig. 18).

PE 85-8. Plug excavation 85-8 was around a plug S-circle and associated plug at ES C (Figs. 8, 19, 20). The circle was on a slope of about 5° and had an oval surface measuring 30 × 45 cm, elongate downslope and carrying small shell fragments. Slabby clasts of the immediately adjacent gravel tended to be on edge, forming a border 10 to 15 cm wide, broadest on the upslope side where there was a 10-cm deep depression in the gravel containing some green and black moss, below which ice was encountered at a depth of 39 cm (8 August 1985). In the gravel on the downslope side of the plug, ice was present at a depth of 49 cm. Assuming the gravel was dry above this depth, the gravel may have been at a freezing temperature a few centimeters higher (cf. PE 90-2).

The area around the plug was then excavated to a depth of 80 cm with the aid of a gasoline-powered PICO chopper. Elongate stones in the plug tended to have their long axis steeply plunging, and slabby stones tended to be on edge, many with flat surfaces parallel to the plug sides. The coherent top of the plug had a 15-cm overhang on the downslope side. The plug had a very firm central area of fines and stones, including much small gravel. Grain-size determinations (Table 2) from the outer part of the plug (Sp. 85-8-8F), compared with the core (Sp. 85-8-8G), showed that the core had appreciably less gravel and more silt. The 8-mm truncated analysis along the core axis indicated a clayey$_{9}$-sandy$_{13}$-gravelly$_{18}$ silt$_{60}$ (M = clayey$_{12}$-sandy$_{16}$ silt$_{73}$), whereas the outer part was a clayey$_{7}$-sandy$_{13}$-gravelly$_{36}$ silt$_{45}$ (M = clayey$_{10}$-sandy$_{20}$ silt$_{70}$).

The plug rested on a 4-cm thick lens of clear ice, containing a few suspended pebbles but free of fines, at a depth of 50 cm, which approximated the plug base and possibly the permafrost table. Such ice may be intrusive (Mackay, 1972, p. 10–11). The lens inclined downslope and thinned both up- and downslope beyond the base. A 4-cm thick frozen layer of fines and gravel separated this lens from a lower one, also 4 cm thick. Continued excavation showed more ice lenses, the largest being 8 to 9 cm

FIGURE 11D. HEAVE CURVES, NE BAR, ES C

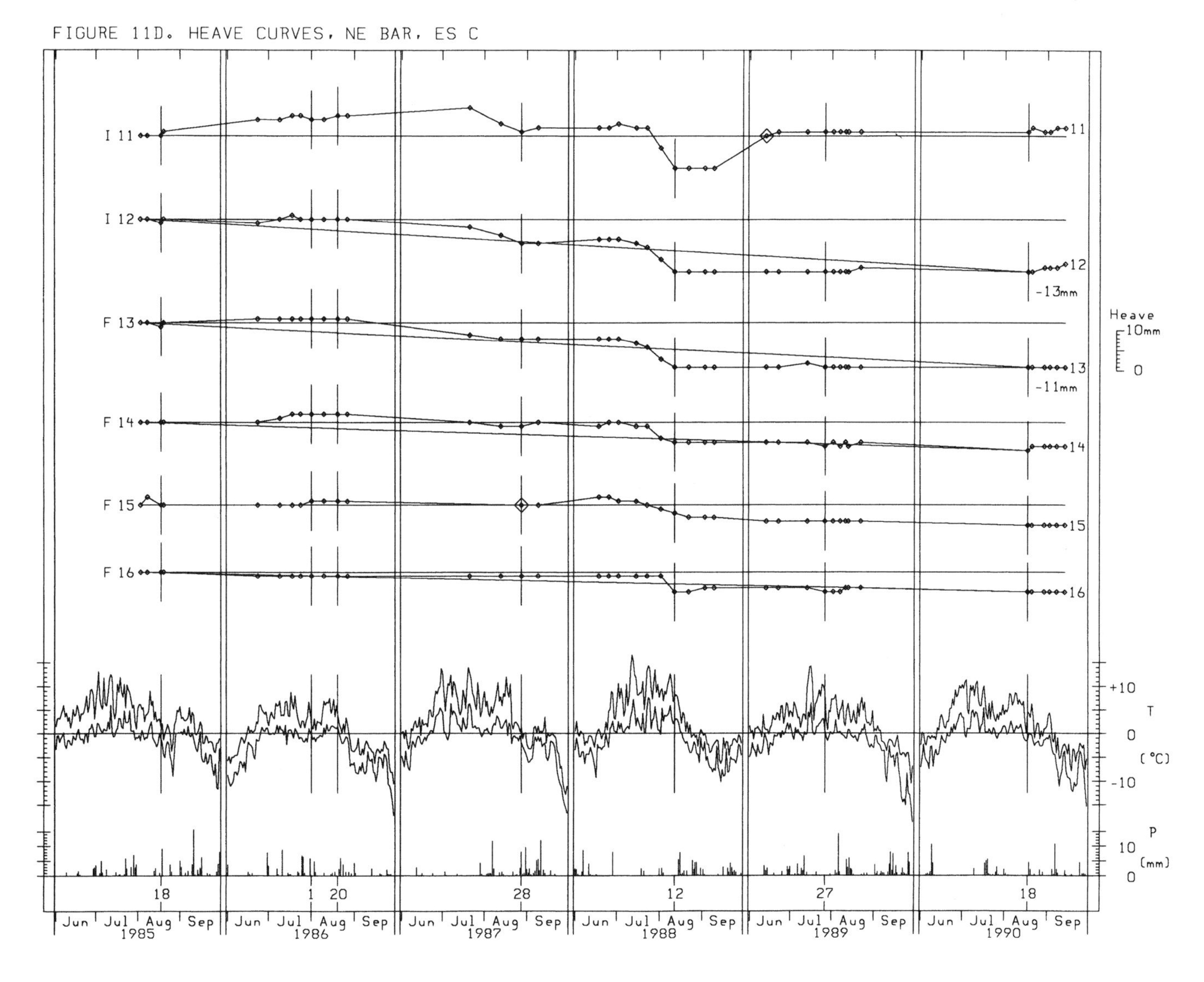

thick; this lens contained some fines and a few stones and shell fragments. Although generally lenslike parallel to the slope, the ice tended to be in irregular masses in detail. Layers of frozen fines with variously oriented ice veinlets separated the lenses. Ice lenses with bubble tubes rising through them and in places containing fines were noted in permafrost at a depth of 70 to 80 cm. In general the ice masses occupied a larger area than the base of the plug.

Shell fragments (*Mya truncata*) from pluglike soil at a depth interval of 50 to 70 cm below the surface and some 0 to 20 cm below the approximate base of the plug and in part outside the projected circumference of the plug, provided a ^{14}C age of 4950 ± 40 B.P. (Appendix C, QL-4068). Shell fragments of *Hiatella arctica* and *Mya truncata* from a depth interval of 0 to 50 cm in the plug had a ^{14}C age of 6180 ± 30 B.P. (QL-4069). The inverse age/depth relation of the two dates is consistent with upward intrusion of the plug from older horizons into younger. This agrees with the ^{14}C age of 4470 ± 150 B.P. (QL-4129) for the fibula of a ringed seal (identified by Professor Robert Rausch, University of Washington) from a depth of 20 cm in the gravel surrounding the plug. The date falls exactly on the midline of the emergence-curve envelope for the area (Washburn and Stuiver, 1985, their Fig. 2, p. 635).

PE 86-4. A cut 2 to 4 m wide was bulldozed up- and downslope immediately south of its enlargement toward PE 82-5 (Fig. 8). The cut was up to 20 to 30 cm deep along an average gradient of some 6° and extended several centimeters below the frost table (12 July 1986). PE 86-4 revealed a number of decapitated plugs in frozen beach gravel. The interstices of the gravel were filled with clear ice; most of the stones were barely touching, and many appeared to be separated by a thin (<1 mm thick) film of ice. The decapitated plugs thawed faster than the icy gravel, presumably because of fines that promoted an unfrozen-water content at negative temperature. Within 2 hr, thaw depth in the plugs

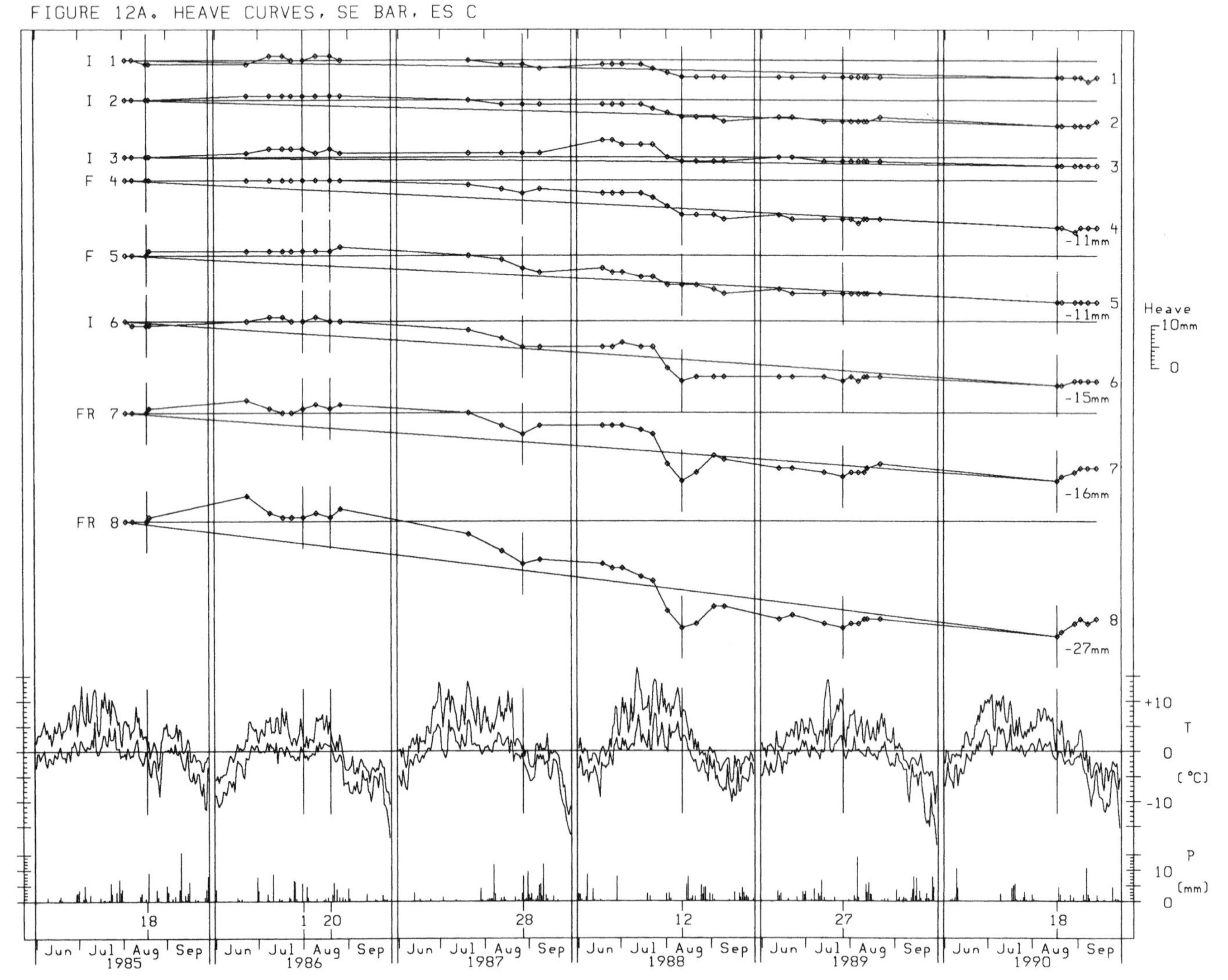

Figures 12A–D (on this and following three pages). Graphs of heaving and settling of ground surface below southeast bar of heave frame, ES C. (For graph construction, see Fig. 11.)

was up to 8 cm, whereas in the gravel it was only 2.5 to 4.5 cm, the deeper thaw being near a plug, the lesser 15 cm from the plug. Within 2 days, thaw depth in the plugs was 13 to 15 cm and 8.0 to 9.7 cm in the gravel. The plugs were most common where the slope decreased, especially opposite PE 82-5. Water here tended to ooze from the decapitated plugs along the contour and also in the cut of PE 86-4 about 5 m upslope from PE 82-5 where a northeast-southwest linear area of fines appeared but no plugs were identified.

In 1987 the bulldozed cut was trenched with a backhoe to, or slightly below, the frost table at a depth of about 50 cm (5 August), which was up to some 85 cm below the original surface along PE 86-4. The trenching exposed a 1-m wide ice wedge on the upslope side of the northeast-southwest linear area of fines at about the 85-cm depth from the original surface. However, removal of the top 30 cm of soil in 1986 and an exceptionally warm summer in 1987 probably led to some lowering of the wedge top. The wedge ice was mainly coarse grained (melt boundaries 1 to 2 cm across), and the wedge had a faint lineation of white bubble zones vertically oriented and more or less parallel to the wedge trend. The bubbles responsible for the lineation were up to about 3 mm long with a cross section of 1 mm, and their elongation was horizontal, normal to the lineation. The ice at the wedge edges tended to be clear. The sediments on the downslope (west) side of the wedge dipped steeply away from it.

Near its upslope termination, PE 86-4 cut across the upper edge of a series of aligned plugs, with the upslope side of a transected plug exhibiting a relief of 25 cm in the surrounding openwork gravel. This gravel extended to a depth of 37 cm some 75 cm upslope from the plug, and the plug did not appear to have any upslope extension but rested directly on "dirty" gravel that contained significantly fewer fines than in the plugs. This gravel underlay the plugs and the openwork surface gravel. The ice content (w_f) of the "dirty" gravel at a depth of some 70 to 75 cm below the 1984 surface and in the then permafrost (5 to 10 cm below the frost table of the deepened excavation on 11 August 1987) was 28% below the plug and 33% below the openwork gravel.

PE 86-6. Located at ES C (Fig. 8), PE 86-6 encompassed

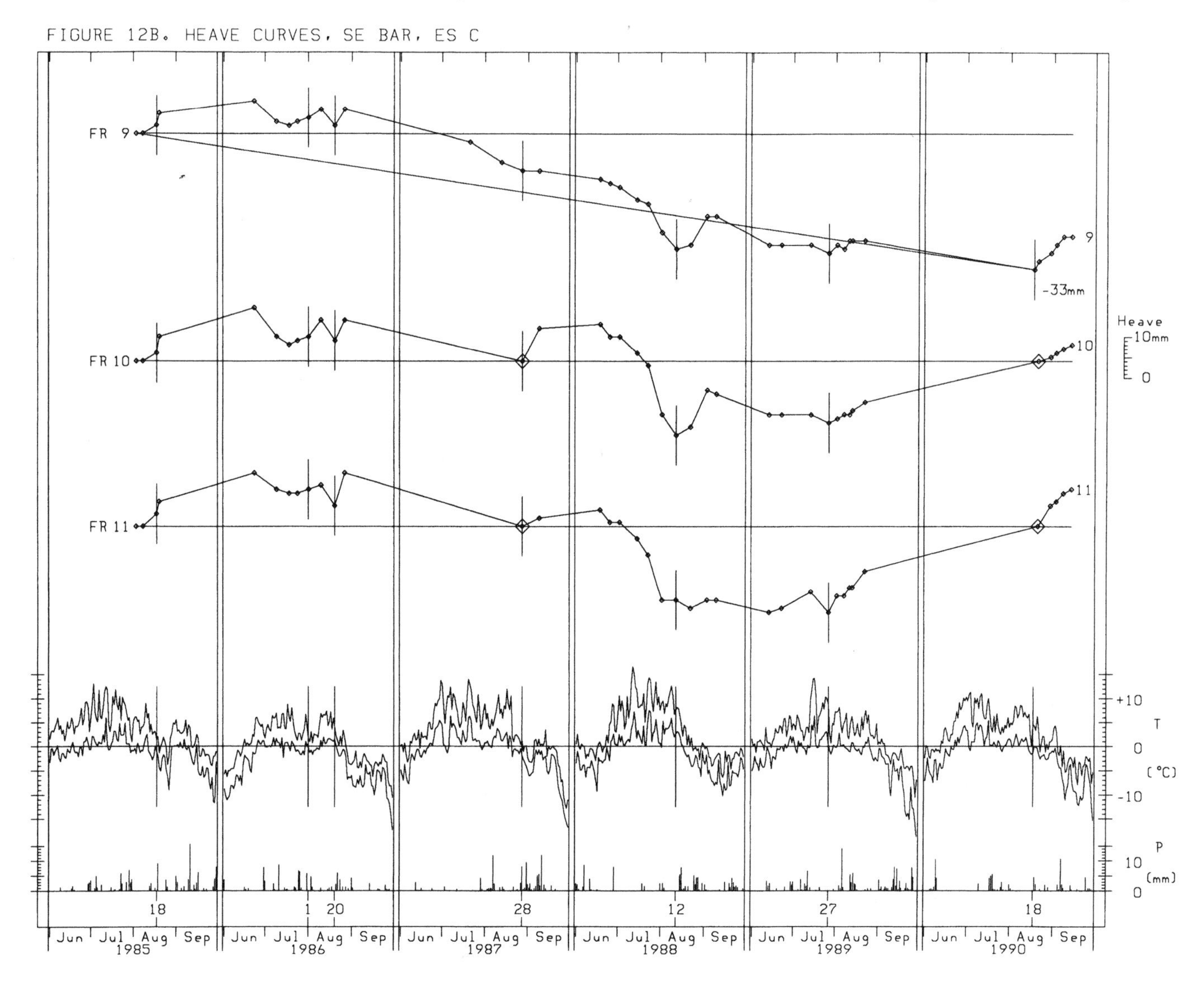

a plug circle and associated plug, the former measuring 25 × 45 cm, elongate downslope along an up- and downslope, east-west furrow 6 to 7 cm deep. The furrow overlay an ice wedge, as shown by the furrow's grading into fresh thermokarst farther downslope where the surface had been bulldozed. Coarser gravel than usual occurred to a depth of 20 cm around the plug, especially on the upslope side, and was present in other nearby patches adjacent to the furrow, as discussed below.

Exhumation of the plug showed that its upslope side leaned 24° downslope and that the downslope side of the top had an overhang, presumably because the concentration of fines thinned downslope, resulting in that side being less cohesive and more subject to sloughing during exhumation. Also as usual the long axes of clasts tended to be vertical, and slabby clasts were commonly on edge with their flat surfaces paralleling plug sides. The frost table in the east-west furrow lay at a depth of 29 cm (12 August 1986) and was 1 to 5 cm deeper at the base of the plug, whereas 50 to 70 cm from the north and south sides of the plug it was 3 to 5 cm shallower (Fig. 21). Thus the frost table in the plug formed a closed depression as usual, but in this case it was elongate, coincident with the surface furrow. The plug had a small neck extending upslope at the gravel frost table, and water was noted on both the up- and downslope sides of the plug but not on the other sides. The plug was very stony with the fines being most obvious near the top and on the upslope side. As was commonly the case in plugs, the fines had numerous voids 1 mm or so in diameter.

Jackhammering 10 cm into the frost table following removal of the thawed part of the plug revealed no ice lenses in the frozen plug; the plug soil at a depth of 30 to 35 cm had an ice content (w_f) of 15% (23 August 1986). The interstices of the surrounding openwork gravel were ice filled.

PE 86-6 had a small circular patch of coarse gravel amid finer gravel at the surface on its north side, about 1 m from the exhumed plug of PE 86-6. Cutting back the gravel revealed an underlying plug top surrounded by a larger area of the coarse gravel. It was clear that a coarse gravel layer had been domed toward the surface and that the plug's continued growth would have enlarged the surface patch of coarse gravel before the plug top itself emerged. Similarly, the upslope neck of PE 86-6 may

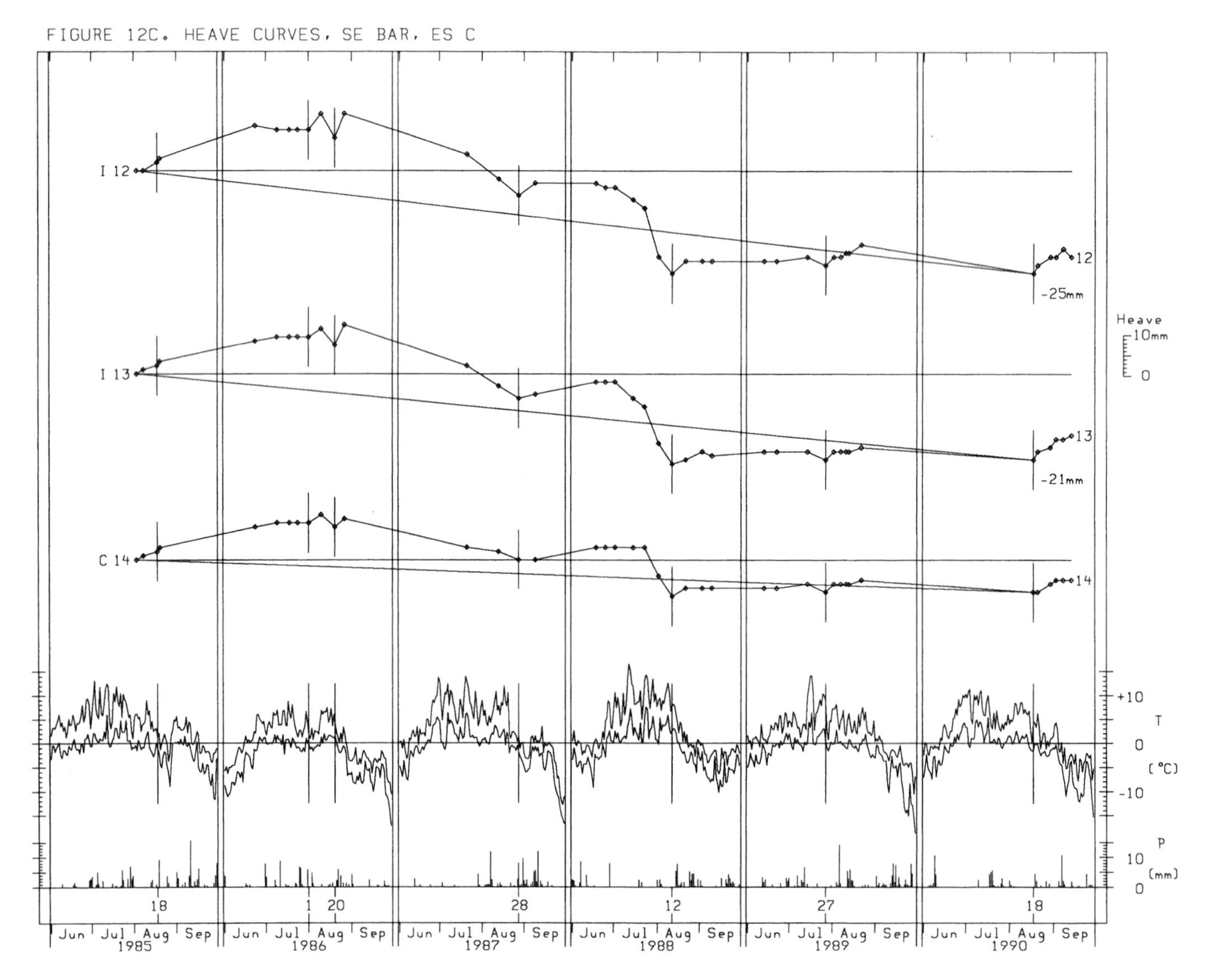

have led to doming and emergence of the relatively coarse gravel overlying the neck. The association of plug necks with overlying gravel concentrations was frequently noted in the Resolute area.

PE 89-1. The excavation of a plug S-circle 4 m south of the heave frame at ES C constituted PE 89-1 (Figs. 8, 22). The circle, elongate up- and downslope on a general gradient of about 5 to 6°, measured 32 × 46 cm and was domed. However, the domed area itself, which had a relief of 6 cm, was larger because the coarse gravel of a subsurface layer had emerged with the plug, a situation similar to that described at PE 86-6.

Probing before excavation and subsequent observations indicated that the frost table was 44 cm below the central area and about 10 cm less below the bordering gravel (17 July 1989). Allowing for the difference in surface relief of 6 cm, the frost table thus lay some 4 cm deeper below the central area than below the border.

Removal of gravel from around the plug revealed on the upslope side a plug neck of fines-rich gravel 10 to 15 cm wide, 65 cm long, and 10 to 30 cm high, the low point being where the neck joined the plug and the high point perhaps being a developing plug (Fig. 23).

Grain-size analyses of the plug (Sps. 89-7-17A–17R), truncated at 8 mm, are given in Table 3. The data do not show a consistent correlation as to location of the greatest concentration of fines except that it tended to be on the upslope side for the specimen as a whole and on the downslope side for the matrix. At the depth of 30 to 40 cm the concentration coincided with the center or core area of both. Ice-contents (w_f) at a depth of about 40 to 45 cm (17 July) were 18% in the plug and 12% in the gravel.

PE 89-2. Plug excavation 89-2 was in an area of well-developed rows of plug S-circles to S-semicircles, downslope from the gravel haul road near its intersection with the VOR road. PE 89-2 trenched the upslope half of one of the best-developed plug S-semicircles (Fig. 24). The S-semicircles here tended to parallel the contour but were commonly slightly offset from each other. The spacing between rows was commonly about 2.5 m, with the S-semicircles commonly also offset from those of the next row, resulting in an overall en-echelon and

FIGURE 12D. HEAVE CURVES, SE BAR, ES C

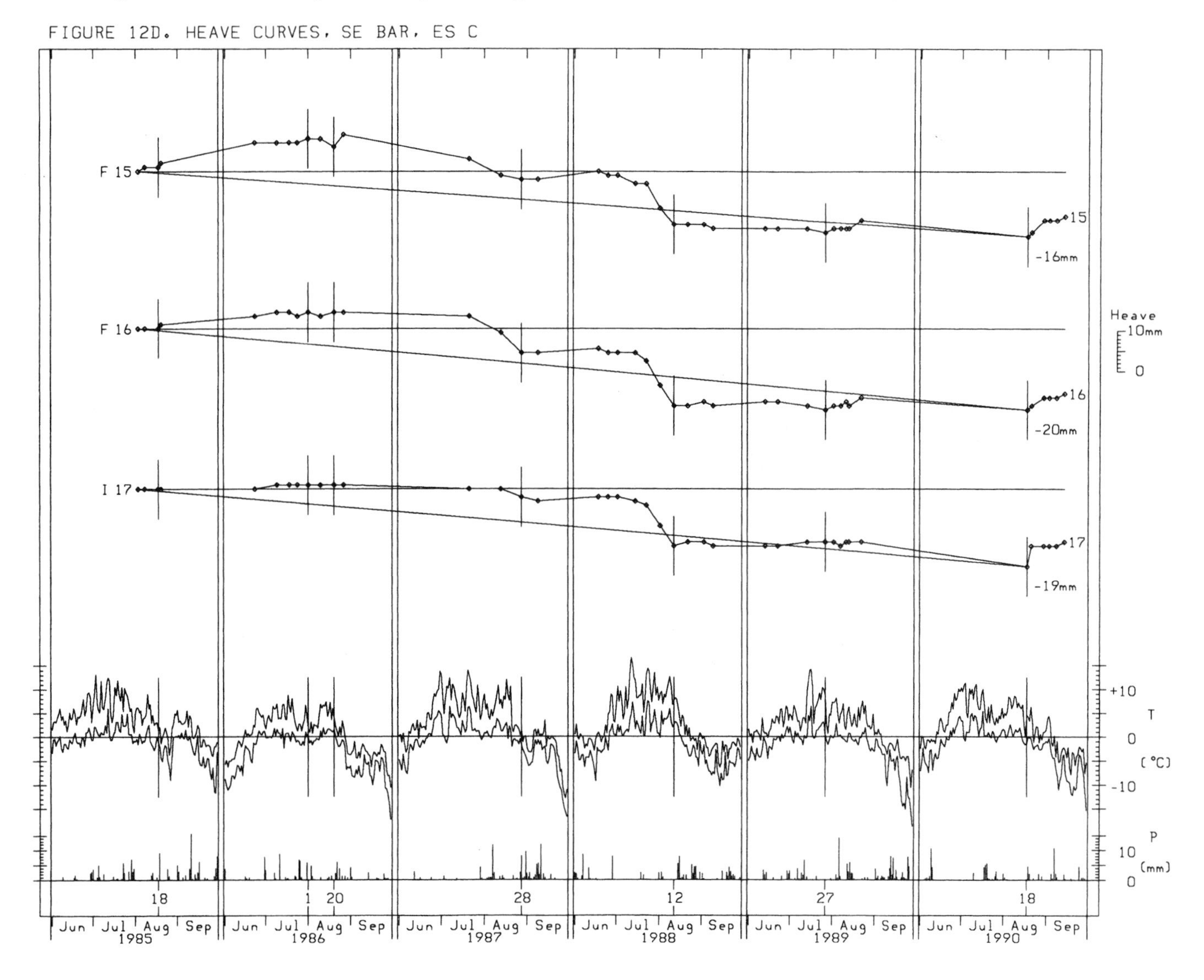

Figure 13. PE 82-5, ES C, 11 July 1982. View east upslope. 16-cm rule as scale.

Figure 14. PE 82-5, ES C, extended 8 September 1982. View south along contour showing plugs, a plug circle by rule at far edge of excavation, and upslope depressions of plug S-semicircles paralleling contour beyond excavation (cf. Fig. 27). 16-cm rule as scale (arrow points to rule). The prominent plug circle in Figure 13 had collapsed. The surface beyond the excavation is crossed diagonally by tractor treads.

Figure 15. PE 82-5, ES C, extended 19 July 1986. View south. 1-m stick and 15-cm rule as scales.

thus anastomosing gravel pattern that carried runoff around the plugs. The gradient of the openwork-gravel slope above the plug complex was 7 to 8° declining to 5° within 5 to 10 cm of PE 89-2. The general gradient across a series of rows was 5 to 6°. The upslope side of the plug S-semicircles had not only a marked relief but also the greatest concentration of gravel. The convex surface and radial cracking of some fines areas and the presence there of occasional small, slightly raised, and now inactive rill channels leading downslope across the convex surfaces strongly suggested recent differential frost heaving of these plug S-semicircles.

Excavation of a small trench across the gradient showed that the plug fines arose from depth along sharply defined and essentially vertical contacts and tapered off downslope upon reaching the surface (Fig. 25). On the upslope side the plug soil "spilled over" only very slightly, and the contact below this was vertical and rimmed with fine gravel. The frost table was at a depth of 30 cm in the openwork gravel; in the fines-rich plug it dipped to 65 cm below the crest of the semicircle (25 July 1989). The plug soil contained a few shell fragments and several gravelly concen-

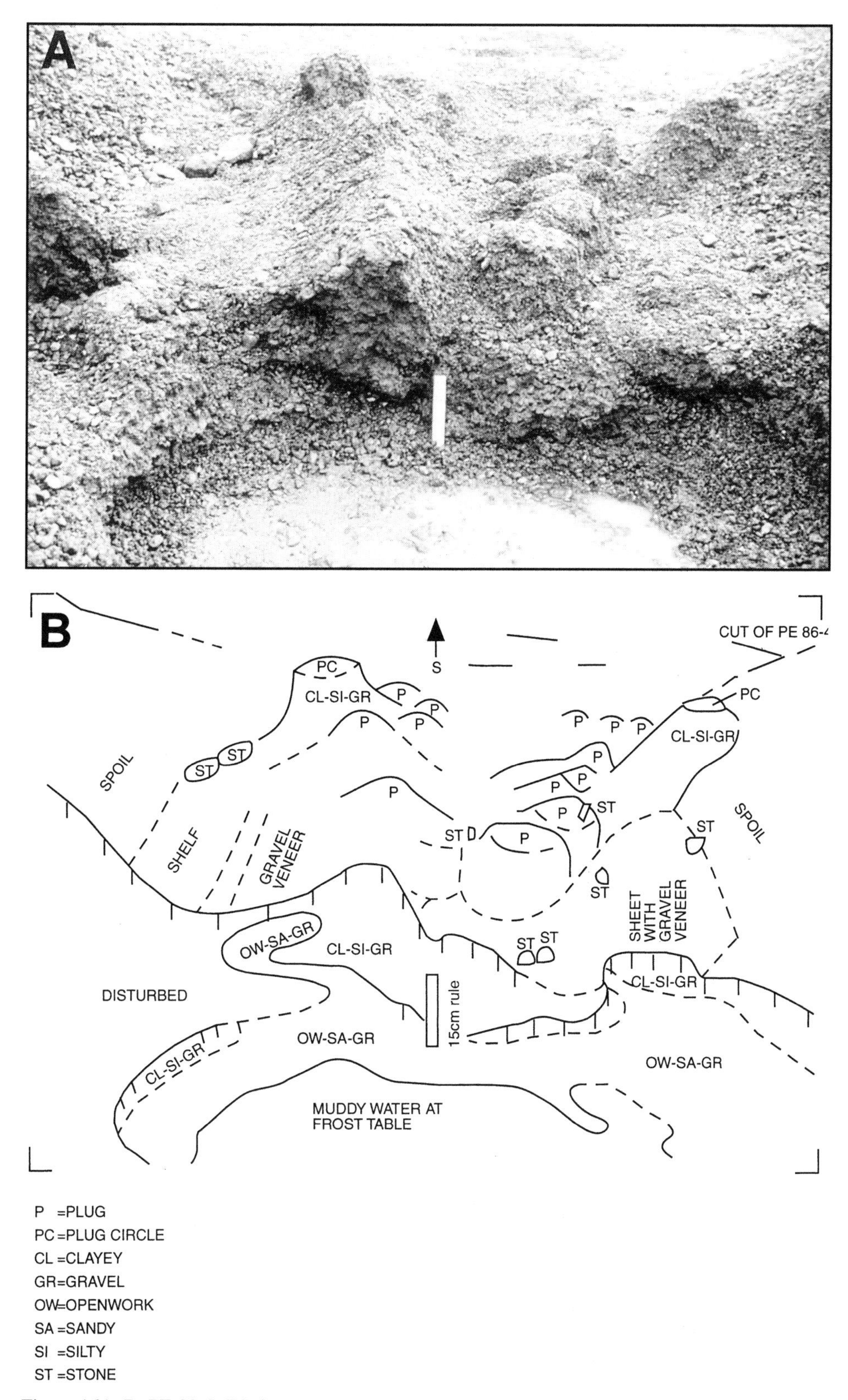

P =PLUG
PC=PLUG CIRCLE
CL =CLAYEY
GR=GRAVEL
OW=OPENWORK
SA =SANDY
SI =SILTY
ST =STONE

Figure 16A–B. PE 82-5, ES C, extended 21 August 1986. View south. PC indicates exhumed plug circles; P designates mainly plugs but includes among the more prominent occurrences several plug circles whose locations were not separately identified.

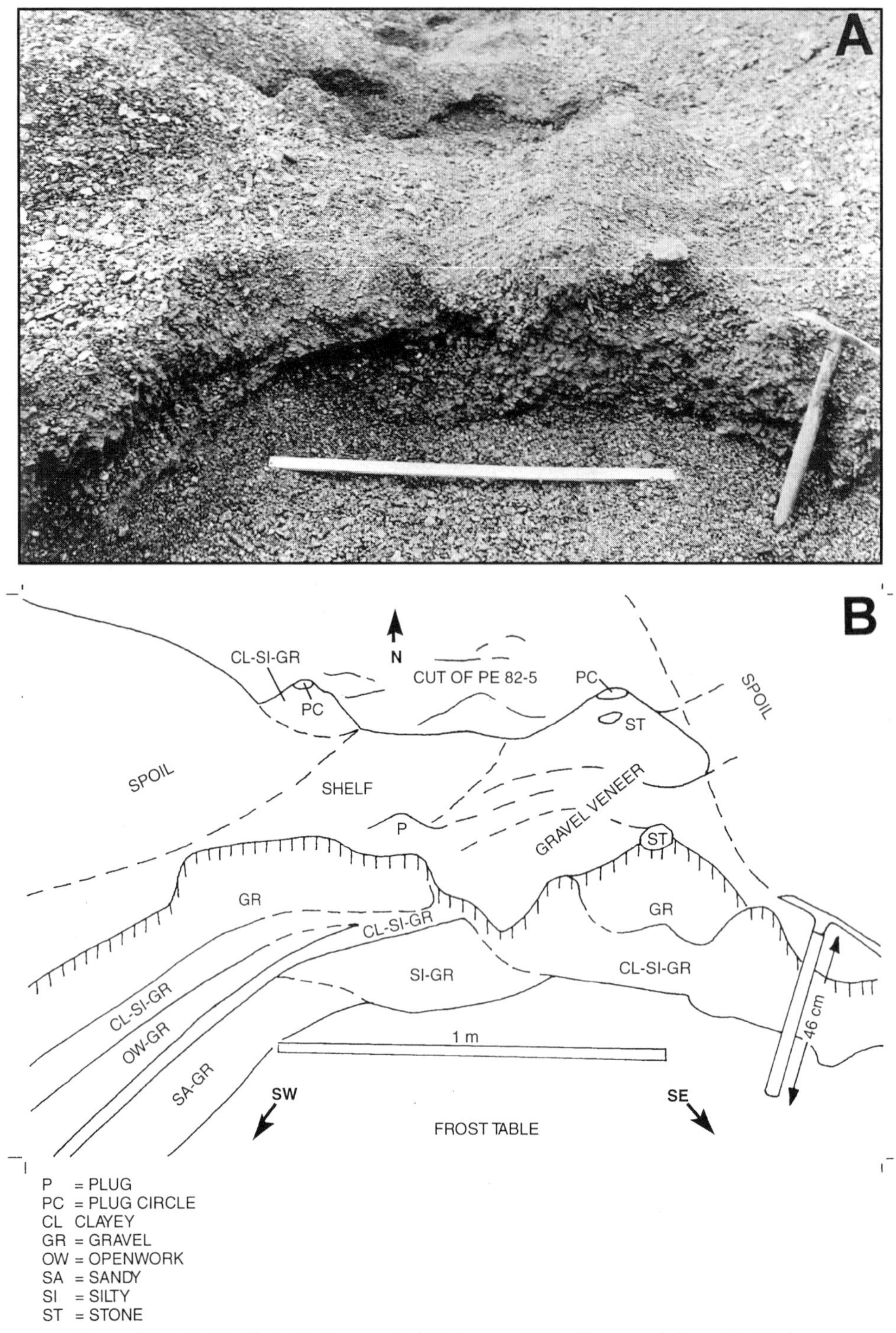

Figure 17A–B. PE 82-5, ES C, extended 24 August 1987. View north from PE 86-4 cut.

trations. Continuation of the excavation upslope for a meter showed that fines-rich gravel similar to that of the plug underlay the openwork gravel at a depth of about 30 cm and had a surface characterized by irregular knoblike rises 1 to 2 cm high.

In cross section the situation was somewhat similar to that described from Spitsbergen by Herz and Andreas (1966, p. 91–94; their Fig. E, Tafel 42), reproduced here as Figure 26.

PE 90-1. Plug excavation 90-1 was started as a shallow up- and downslope, bulldozed trench whose upper end lay some 230 m northwest of ES C (Fig. 8). The trench was across a prominent bench whose altitude at PE 90-1 was about 23 m. PE 90-1 was subsequently deepened with a backhoe, the last time in 1990 when a plug (Sp. 90-8-24) was exhumed and collected for fabric study. The excavation provided cross sections of

Figure 18. PE 82-6, ES C. Plug neck extending upslope. 16-cm rule as scale.

Figure 20. PE 85-8, ES C. View downslope. 15-cm rule at upper left as scale (arrow points to rule).

Figure 19. PE 85-8, ES C. Plug S-circle 3 m upslope from north end of PE 82-5. View north prior to excavation. 15-cm rule on downslope side of circle as scale.

plugs and associated circles aligned in rows that characterized the bench surface (Fig. 27), which had a general gradient of 3 to 4°. The rows were commonly parallel to each other, but in places two adjacent rows converged into one. Overall the rows were in en-echelon pattern at a slight angle to the inner edge of the bench. Commonly the upslope side of individual circles had the greatest relief, and some of the circles qualified as plug S-semicircles; the latter also had the greatest concentration of stones as well as the freshest appearance. Similar plug rows were cited in connection with PE 89-2; their origin is discussed later in the section "Characteristics of Plugs and Plug Circles, Pattern: Discussion, 1a through 1c."

The north side of the expanded trench exhibited plugs in openwork gravel. The gravel reached a depth of about 55 cm (Fig. 28), and the plugs, some of which tended to lean slightly upslope, were underlain by fines-rich gravel with zones of coarse dirty gravel. The fines-rich gravel was underlain in turn by largely openwork gravel that graded downward to shelly sandy gravel with spotty openwork texture.

The south side of PE 90-1 exposed openwork dolomitic

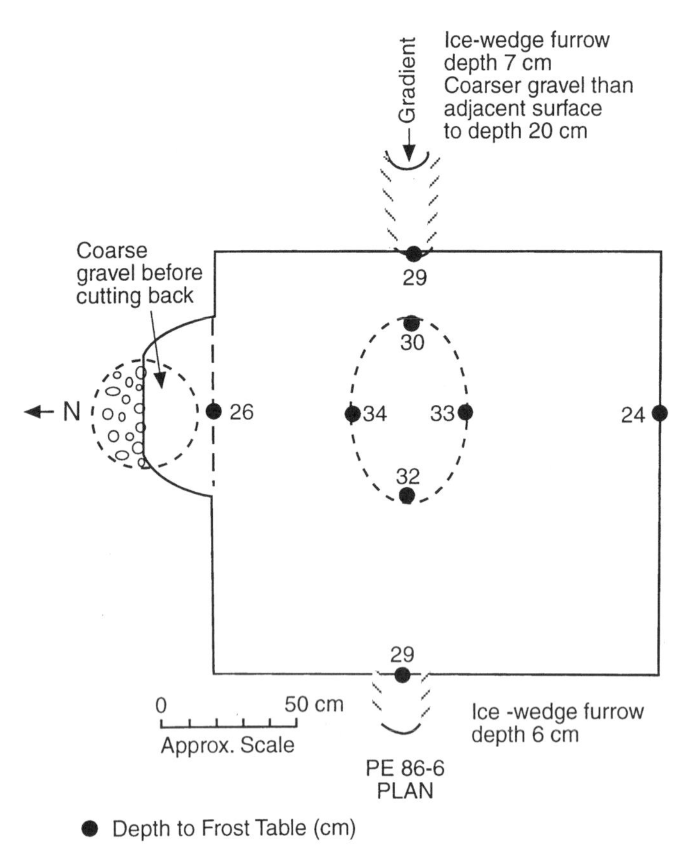

Figure 21. Plan of PE 86-6, ES C, at frost table (12 August 1986).

Figure 22. PE 89-1, ES C. View east upslope prior to excavation. 16-cm rule as scale.

gravel surrounding plugs to a depth of 40 to 45 cm. Contrary to the gravel, the plug fines reacted quite vigorously to HCl (10% solution). Below some 45 cm, a layer of fines-rich gravel, 10 to 15 cm thick (Fig. 29), overlay "dirty" but comparatively openwork sandy gravel with many shell fragments. Depth to the frost (permafrost?) table in the center of nearby plug S-circles beyond the trench was about 60 cm (57 to 62 cm by probing) and 45 cm in the openwork gravel (26 July 1989). The general 60-cm depth to which the fines-rich gravel reached in the trench may approximate the pretrench permafrost table. The lowerlying, comparatively openwork gravel was consistent with the depth and nature of the ice-rich gravel associated with the top of the permafrost at ES C.

The plugs were continuous with the layer of fines-rich gravel, and in some sections, as the exposure was cut back, the plugs revealed a slight upslope lean (Fig. 29, right side), similar to their tendency on the north side of the trench (Fig. 28). Plug fabrics were characterized by tabular and elongate stones tending to lie in a vertical plane with the short axis of tabular stones near the plug periphery being oriented normal to the periphery.

In the field, Sp. 90-8-24 from the south side of PE 90-1 had a height of 45 cm from its bottom at a layer of fines-rich gravel (Fig. 30). However, only the top 42 cm were analyzed.

Grain-size data truncated at 8 mm and bulk density for Sp. 90-8-24 are given in Table 5 along with comparable data for

Figure 23. PE 89-1, ES C. View south. 1-m stick and 16-cm rule as scales.

Figure 24. PE 89-2, downslope from gravel haul road near intersection with VOR road. View north prior to excavation. 1-m stick on upslope edge of plug S-semicircle as scale.

Sp. 90-9-3A at PE 90-2 and are discussed with PE 90-2 for ease of comparison. Similarly, the fabric of Sp. 90-8-24 at PE 90-1 and of Sp. 90-9-3A at PE 90-2 are reviewed together below.

PE 90-2. Plug excavation 90-2 was at an altitude of about 16 m on the north side of ES C (Fig. 8). The surface of the associated plug S-circle was more moist (darker colored) on the upslope than the downslope and lateral sides, and it had a few tiny shell fragments. The surrounding clasts were dolomitic, but the plug fines reacted quite vigorously to HCl (10%).

The plug (Sp. 90-9-3A) was exhumed to a depth of 38 to 40 cm, where it broke and was extracted. The tops of three frozen small satellite plugs had appeared at a depth of 25 to 30 cm (3 September 1990), and a fourth frozen plug top, extending upward 6 to 7 cm into loose "dirty" gravel, appeared at a depth of about 38 cm (4 September 1990) as the excavation was deepened and widened to diameters ranging from some 170 to 185 cm (Fig. 31). The gravel surrounding the frozen plugs, although loose, would have been ice cemented had there been sufficient moisture. This was determined by rapidly excavating another frozen plug in a test excavation 4 m distant in which the plug was frozen throughout, although ice-cemented gravel was not encountered until the depth of 41 cm where its temperature was –1.2 °C (29.8 °F). Excavation of the main plug site was con-

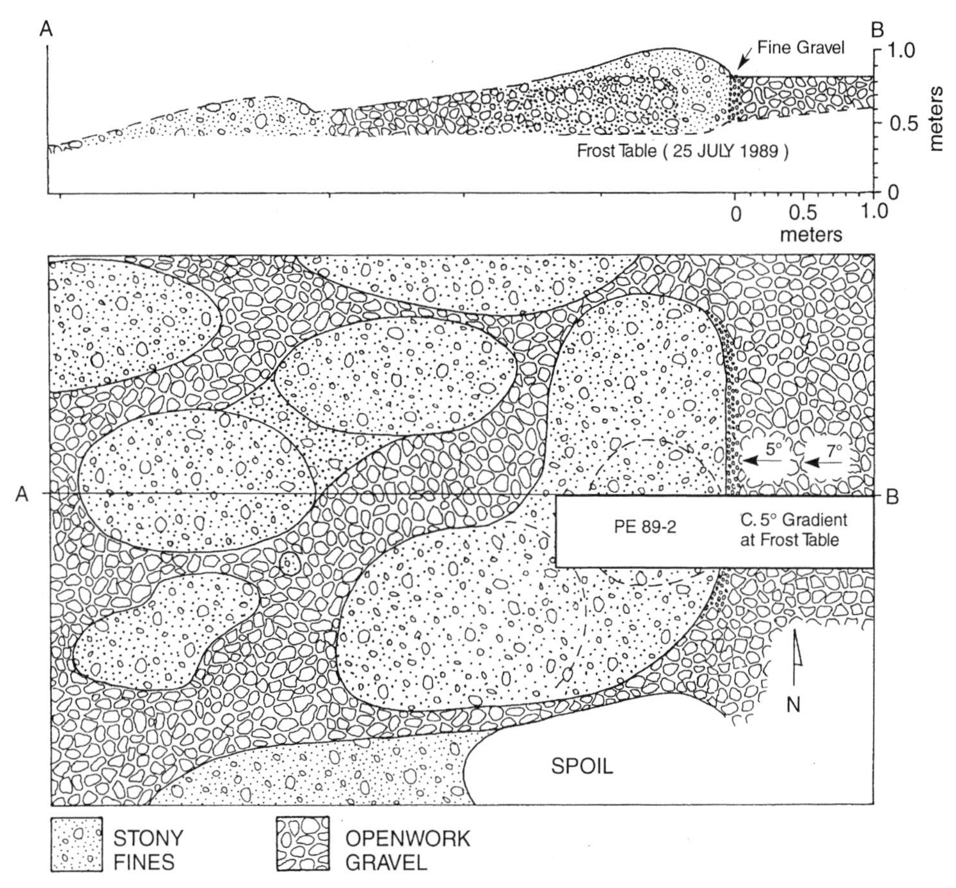

Figure 25. PE 89-2, downslope from gravel haul road near intersection with VOR road. Sketch of excavation area and its relation to exposures of fines-rich gravel surrounded by gravel areas that served as drainage lines.

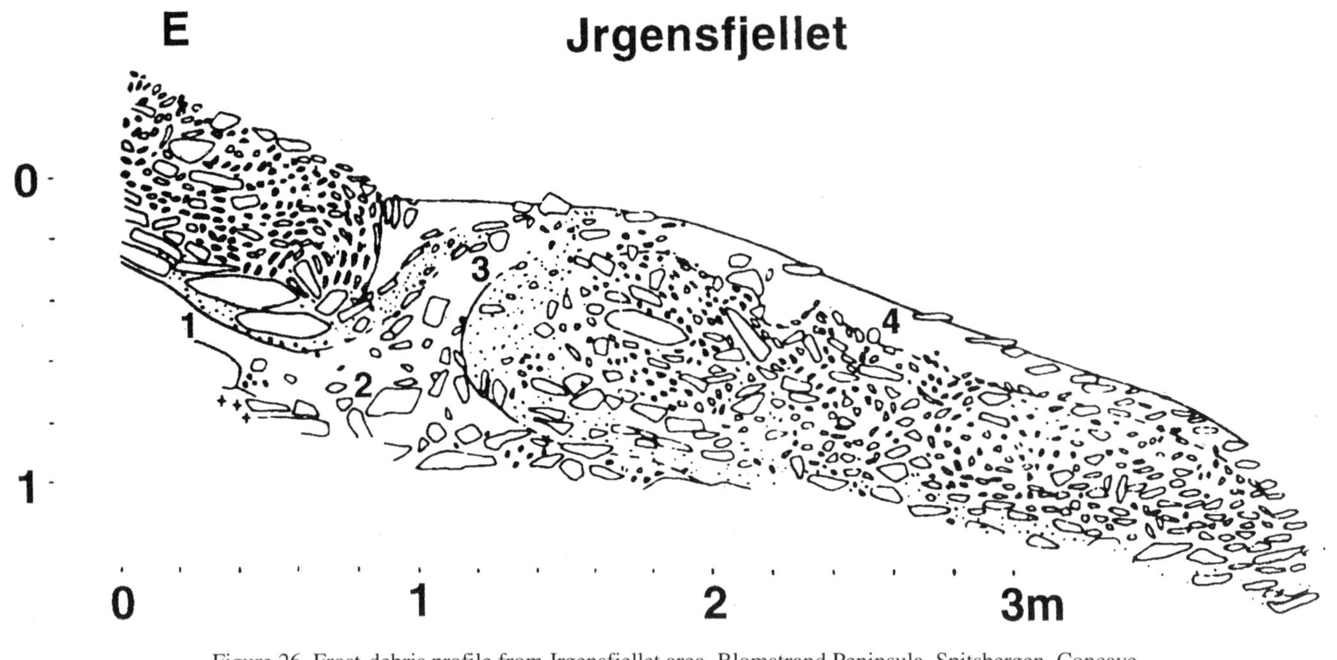

Figure 26. Frost-debris profile from Jrgensfjellet area, Blomstrand Peninsula, Spitsbergen. Concave limestone slope, southwest exposure, 360 m NN, gradient 22 to 15°. Long profile through fine-soil hump. Fine soil of plug base (Steq) (1 and 2) gray brown, of plug top and cover (Decke) (3 and 4) brown. Ice between basal rock fragments identified by crosses on the bottom left side of the figure (Herz and Andreas, 1966, their Fig. E, Tafel 42; see p. 91–94).

tinued with a PICO jackhammer. In addition to the plug of Sp. 90-9-3A, six other plugs were exposed—the four plugs noted above and two plugs whose tops lay within 6 cm of the surface. The site from which Sp. 90-9-3A was extracted left a pit that was enlarged to 46 × 60 cm and a depth of 75 cm (±2 cm).

The ice content (w_f) from a depth of 38 to 48 cm at the site of the extracted plug was 13%; at a depth of 40 to 41 cm between the main plug site and an adjacent small plug, it was 21%. Deepening the excavation also revealed a series of ice lenses along most of the south and southwest faces of the expanded excavation. At a depth of 49 cm (±1 cm), there was an essentially horizontal 2-cm-thick ice lens that had extended into the area below the base of Sp. 90-9-3A. The lens had numerous vertical bubble streaks, and immediately above it were irregular smaller ice lenses commonly less than 1 mm thick, irregular ice "blobs" up to 0.5 cm thick, and small round voids 1 to 3 mm in diameter. A second ice lens, about 1 cm thick and less continuous, was 2 cm below the first. Some 5 cm lower there was more ice than soil over a depth interval of some 6 cm (ca. 59 to 65 cm, probably in permafrost), with an ice content (w_f) of 71%. Some of this ice had very thin (<1 mm thick) vertical streaks, but much of it was clear and irregular amid "dirty" pebble gravel. The ice content at a depth of 65 to 75 cm was 38%.

Since all the soil was at a negative temperature below a depth of 40 cm or less in early September, and the permafrost table here was probably shallower than 60 cm as suggested by the ice concentrations and their nature, it would appear there had been a considerable amount of upward freezing from the permafrost table. This would be consistent with other excavations and observations at ES C.

Figure 27. Plug S-circle and plug S-semicircle rows on bench trenched by PE 90-1, about 230 m northwest of ES C. View south. Person as scale.

As shown in Table 5, the bulk densities of Sp. 90-8-24 from PE 90-1 and of Sp. 90-9-3A from PE 90-2 were very similar, as were the grain-size analyses—truncated at 8 mm.

Table 6 shows the plunges of stones with the long axis exceeding the intermediate axis by at least 50% (a > 1.50 b). Of the total number of such stones measured in Sp. 90-8-24 (N = 68),

Figure 28. PE 90-1, bench (trenched by PE 90-1), about 230 m northwest of ES C. View north. 1-m stick (resting on frozen ground below original permafrost table) and 16-cm rule as scales.

plunges of 70 to 79° constituted the largest class, being 22% of all the stones measured. Forty-five% of the plunges exceeded 50°. In Sp. 90-9-3A (N = 65), plunges of 70 to 79° were again the largest class, being 23% of all the stones measured. To what extent such steep plunges result from upfreezing of stones within a plug, from movement of a plug during upward freezing from the permafrost table, from the plasticity of a plug while freezing, or from a combination of such events does not appear to be known. All these possibilities and perhaps others require further research.

PE 95-1. This plug excavation, immediately south of the heave frame at ES C (Fig. 8), exhumed a plug (Sp. 95-8-20-1 series) to obtain information on variations in grain size. The lettered locations of specimens (Fig. 32; Tables 7 and 8) show percent fines (clay + silt) of the coherent plug after the loosely adhering gravel sloughed off. The analyses of this plug and of the next two (PE 95-2, Sp. 95-8-20-2 series, and PE 95-3, Sp. 95-8-21 series) were carried out by Deepa Spaeth at the Soils Laboratory of the Department of Geography of the University of British Columbia, courtesy of Professor Michael Church, director of the Laboratory. The work was supervised by Sidney Tsang.

The data from PE 95-1 are discussed below together with the data from PE 95-2 and PE 95-3.

PE 95-2. PE 95-2 provided the Sp. 95-8-20-2 series from the bulldozed trench, the site of PE 90-1 where plugs had been collected for fabric study. PE 95-2 was on the south side of the trench within 2 to 3 m of PE 90-1. As at PE 95-1, the lettered locations of specimens (Fig. 33; Tables 9 and 10) show percent fines (clay + silt) of the coherent plug after the loosely adhering gravel sloughed off.

PE 95-3. Located at ES C, PE 95-3 (Fig. 34, Sp. 95-8-21 series) was 3 m north of the northeast end post of the heave frame (Fig. 8). The plug circle was smaller than the circles at PE 95-1 and PE 95-2, but the plug diameter increased at depth. Again, as with the plugs at PE 95-1 and PE 95-2, the lettered locations of specimens (Fig. 35; Tables 11 and 12) indicate the percent fines (clay + silt) of the coherent plug after the loosely adhering gravel sloughed off.

Discussion. The grain-size analyses of the Sp. 95-8-20-1 series from PE 95-1, the Sp. 95-8-20-2 series from PE 95-2, and the Sp. 95-8-21 series from PE 95-3 confirm visual impressions that fines (clay + silt) of a plug tend to increase from the periphery to the core of a plug. These plugs also show a consistent upward increase in core fines, both in nontruncated and truncated analyses. This trend supports the view that in addition to frost heaving of fines from near the permafrost table as inferred from field excavations (for instance, at PE 90-1), plug fines also accumulate higher in the profile. This could include fines moving downslope along the frost table, any fines accompanying surfaceward seepage, and in-situ weathering of larger particles, especially the solution of impure carbonates.

The nontruncated data from the plugs PE 95-1, PE 95-2, and PE 95-3 (Figs. 32, 33, 35; Tables 7, 9, 11) emphasize their high gravel content, especially the specimen series from PE 95-3 (Fig. 35; Table 11).

Dye experiments

Several dye experiments (DE) were conducted in the ES C area in 1986, utilizing fluorescein powder (TD-160) in a concentration of at least a heaping teaspoon in 400 ml of water.

Figure 29. PE 90-1, bench (trenched by PE 90-1), about 230 m northwest of ES C. View south. 1-m stick and 16-cm rule as scales. Top of 16-cm rule indicates the general base of clayey-silty gravel overlying comparatively openwork gravel that is falling away from the more cohesive clayey-silty gravel.

Figure 30. PE 90-1, bench (trenched by PE 90-1) about 230 m northwest of ES C. South side of trench as extended 24 August 1990 prior to removal of plug (Sp. 90-8-24) for fabric analysis. View south showing relation to irregular rows of plugs and plug semicircles. 16-cm rule on top of plug circle as scale.

Figure 31. PE 90-2, ES C. View southwest. 16-cm rule on plug top (Sp. 90-9-3A) as scale. Exhumed height of Sp. 90-9-3A was 38 to 40 cm, with bottom at approximate depth to ice-cemented horizon outside plug base and depth of transition from openwork gravel to underlying "dirty" gravel. At left are three satellite plugs whose tops were ice-cemented at depth of 25 to 30 cm. The openwork gravel surrounding the plug and the three satellite plugs at this depth was loose but at negative temperature.

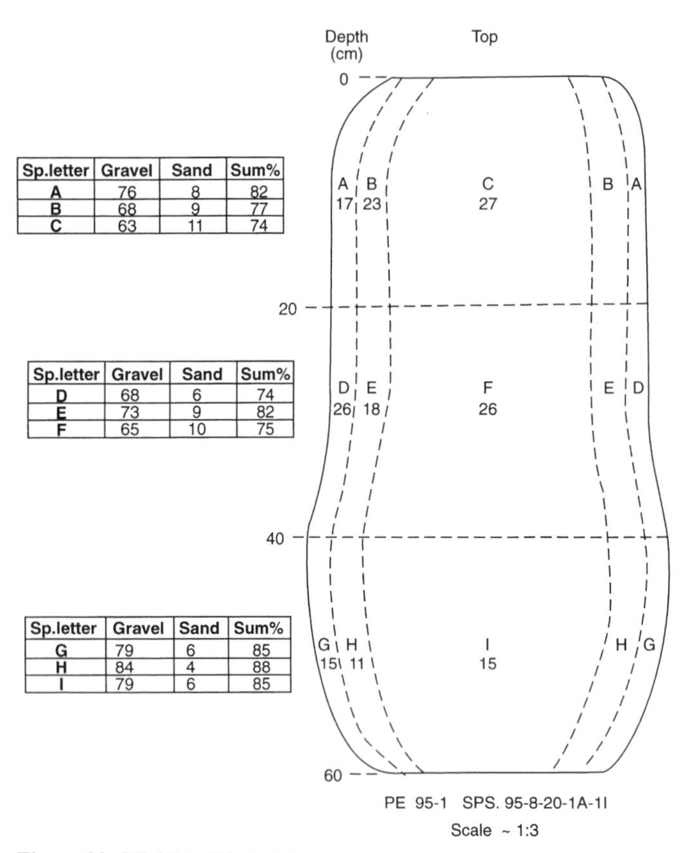

Sp.letter	Gravel	Sand	Sum%
A	76	8	82
B	68	9	77
C	63	11	74

Sp.letter	Gravel	Sand	Sum%
D	68	6	74
E	73	9	82
F	65	10	75

Sp.letter	Gravel	Sand	Sum%
G	79	6	85
H	84	4	88
I	79	6	85

Figure 32. PE 95-1, ES C. Diagram of lengthwise-oriented, dissected plug half (Sp. 95-8-20-1 series) showing location (by specimen letter) of nontruncated analyses as listed in Table 7. Numbers at lettered locations in diagram indicate percent fines (clay + silt). The associated percent gravel and sand is tabulated alongside the diagram. Departures from 100% in total gravel, sand, and fines are due to rounding.

DE 86-1. In the first experiment the dye solution was poured into the beach gravel 15 cm upslope from a plug S-circle 3 m above PE 85-8 (Fig. 8), the intervening gradient being 7°. Depths to the frost table in a plug near the dye insertion point and in the adjacent gravel were, respectively, 27 cm and 19 to 20 cm (14 July 1986). Within less than 30 min the dye appeared in water that lay in the approximately 75-cm deep depression left by PE 85-8. The dye rose from the bottom of the depression in discontinuous swirls, and by the time the depression had drained, days later, it was noticed that silt, some sand, and tiny shell flakes had formed a 4-cm-thick, miniature deltalike deposit where the dye solution had exited from the gravel. Some hours after the dye had appeared in the depression it also appeared 3 m farther downslope in the muddy debris of a decapitated plug in the depression left by PE 85-8. The dye also rose in the plug immediately downslope from the point of dye insertion, but the soil there was drier, and the dye was not noted until 2 weeks later although it may have appeared considerably sooner.

DE 86-2. The next dye experiment was carried out some 10 m south of PE 86-4. The dye solution was inserted where trickling meltwater from a snowbank was disappearing into gravel whose thaw depth was 22 to 23 cm (14 July 1986). The dye appeared at the frost table (depth 18 cm) 5 m downslope 8 min later. The intervening gradient was 11°. In another 15 min the dye emerged at the surface 10 m farther downslope where thaw water was appearing at the base of a bulldozer cut, the intervening gradient being 8°. Seven hours later the water was clear.

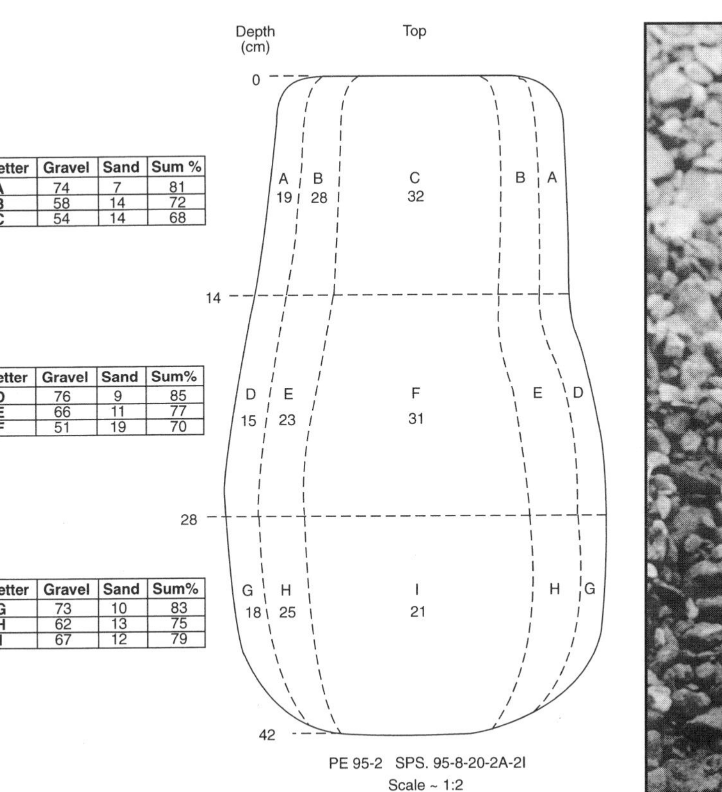

Sp.letter	Gravel	Sand	Sum %
A	74	7	81
B	58	14	72
C	54	14	68

Sp.letter	Gravel	Sand	Sum%
D	76	9	85
E	66	11	77
F	51	19	70

Sp.letter	Gravel	Sand	Sum%
G	73	10	83
H	62	13	75
I	67	12	79

Figure 33. PE 95-2, bench (trenched by PE 90-1) about 230 m northeast of ES C. Diagram of lengthwise-oriented, dissected plug half (Sp. 95-8-20-2 series) showing location (by specimen letter) of nontruncated analyses as listed in Table 9. Numbers at lettered locations in diagram indicate percent fines (clay + silt). The associated percent gravel and sand is tabulated alongside the diagram. Departures from 100% in total gravel, sand, and fines are due to rounding.

Figure 34. PE 95-3, ES C. View east (upslope). 16-cm rule as scale on plug top prior to removal of plug (Sp. 95-8-21 series) for grain-size analyses.

Observations at Sheringham Point

On the lower slopes of Sheringham Point, north of Resolute, the surfaces of emerged beaches are almost totally disrupted by EB S-circles. Although the beaches are obvious from the air, on the ground they are primarily manifested by the circles aligned parallel to them. Judging from the many excavations of identical-appearing circles elsewhere, these are plug S-circles.

White chert is characteristic of some of the local bedrock, and at one site above the lower slopes a series of EB S-circles was characterized by concentrations of angular chert fragments whose color contrasted with the generally darker, surrounding surface. Since the fragments were essentially confined to the circles rather than being more widely scattered, the circles were almost certainly underlain by plugs that were carrying up fragments from underlying disintegrating bedrock.

OCCURRENCES IN MISCELLANEOUS DEPOSITS

Excavations

PE 81-1. Plug S-circles occur at an altitude of about 75 m some 350 m southwest of the North Transmitter Station. North–south–striking and steeply east-dipping, disintegrating, dolomite bedrock crops out in the immediate area, and bedrock is generally close to the surface or at it. Most of the surface debris consists of angular clasts from the local bedrock. Also present are fines, shell fragments, and erratics of ice-rafted and/or glacial origin. PE 81-1 was excavated across a plug S-circle in this debris. Only a conical tip of stony fines had reached the surface as an S-circle 20 cm in diameter, which was bordered by slabby angular gravel that tended to be on edge with flat sides paralleling the plug sides and forming an encircling rim 15 to 30 cm wide, with little if any relief and with mostly flat-lying smaller stones extending beyond it (Fig. 36). The rim consisted of clasts from depth, domed by the plug. The frost table in the plug lay at a depth of 46 cm (29 July 1981). Excavation continued intermittently to 19 August, by which time thawing had reached a depth of 60 to 65 cm.

The completed excavation showed a plug amid mainly openwork gravel except at the maximum depth of excavation, where silt and clay became abundant. The location and grain-

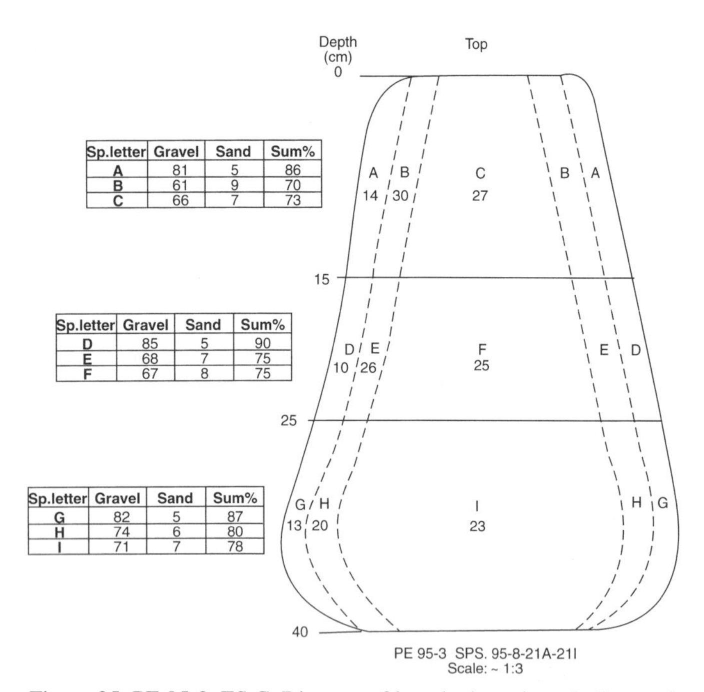

Sp.letter	Gravel	Sand	Sum%
A	81	5	86
B	61	9	70
C	66	7	73

Sp.letter	Gravel	Sand	Sum%
D	85	5	90
E	68	7	75
F	67	8	75

Sp.letter	Gravel	Sand	Sum%
G	82	5	87
H	74	6	80
I	71	7	78

Figure 35. PE 95-3, ES C. Diagram of lengthwise-oriented, dissected plug half (Sp. 95-8-21 series) showing location (by specimen letter) of nontruncated analyses as listed in Table 11. Numbers at lettered locations in diagram indicate percent fines (clay + silt). The associated percent gravel and sand is tabulated alongside the diagram. Departures from 100% in total gravel, sand, and fines are due to rounding. The basal flattening of the specimen below the depth of 37 cm does not represent the in-situ plug shape (Fig. 34) but reflects subsequent deformation.

Figure 36. PE 81-1 about 350 m southwest of North Transmitter Station, prior to excavation. View east (upslope). 16-cm rule as scale.

size analyses of nontruncated specimens are summarized in Figures 37 and 38 and Table 13. The analyses (Fig. 38) show fines along the core axis decreasing from 39% at a depth of 10 to 15 cm to 25% at a depth of 40 to 45 cm, then increasing to 51% at the maximum depth of excavation (60 to 65 cm). The

Figure 37. PE 81-1 about 350 m southwest of North Transmitter Station. Depth 60 to 65 cm showing location of Sp. 81-8-19 series. Water had infiltrated bottom of excavation prior to photograph. 16-cm rule as scale.

latter depth was probably below the 1981 permafrost table here, in view of intermittent removal of thawed soil until 19 August. An overall increase in fines at or near the top of the plug and near the permafrost table appeared to be general, as in a number of other excavations but not all (cf. PE 95-1, 95-3).

The thawed fines in the top part of the plug to at least the 30-cm depth had prominent vesicles, especially adjacent to stones. Granules were increasingly common near the stony borders. A very stony plug was noted on one side of the excavation.

PE 82-1. A series of plug excavations was made at an altitude of some 65 to 70 m northeast of the North Transmitter Station where the generally even terrain begins to steepen before descending abruptly to form the south bank of McMaster River. The surface was characterized by plug S-circles of fines-rich gravel surrounded by stones, including angular, gray-weathering limestone and tan-weathering dolomite fragments from the near-surface bedrock. The area lay below the Holocene marine limit and, as at PE 81-1, shell fragments were common and there were occasional erratics. Lichens were common on surficial stones. The plug circles were well developed. They commonly had the coarsest debris in their vicinity concentrated on their upslope side and associated with an irregular plug pit. All the plugs excavated in the area were exhumed to the frost table and cut back sequentially.

PE 82-1 was illustrative of well-developed forms in the area. The circle had a central area of fines-rich gravel some 30 cm in diameter and a convex surface with a relief of 5 cm. In common with a number of plugs, there appeared to be a concentration of fines in the top 5 cm. The frost table (27 June 1982) in the surrounding openwork gravel was at a depth of 12 to 15 cm, below which the gravel had interstitial ice. In the plug near its edge, depth to the frost table was 17 cm, increasing to 26 cm at its core. Further excavation showed that the plug was connected to an upslope plug neck at least 13 cm long, and both the plug and

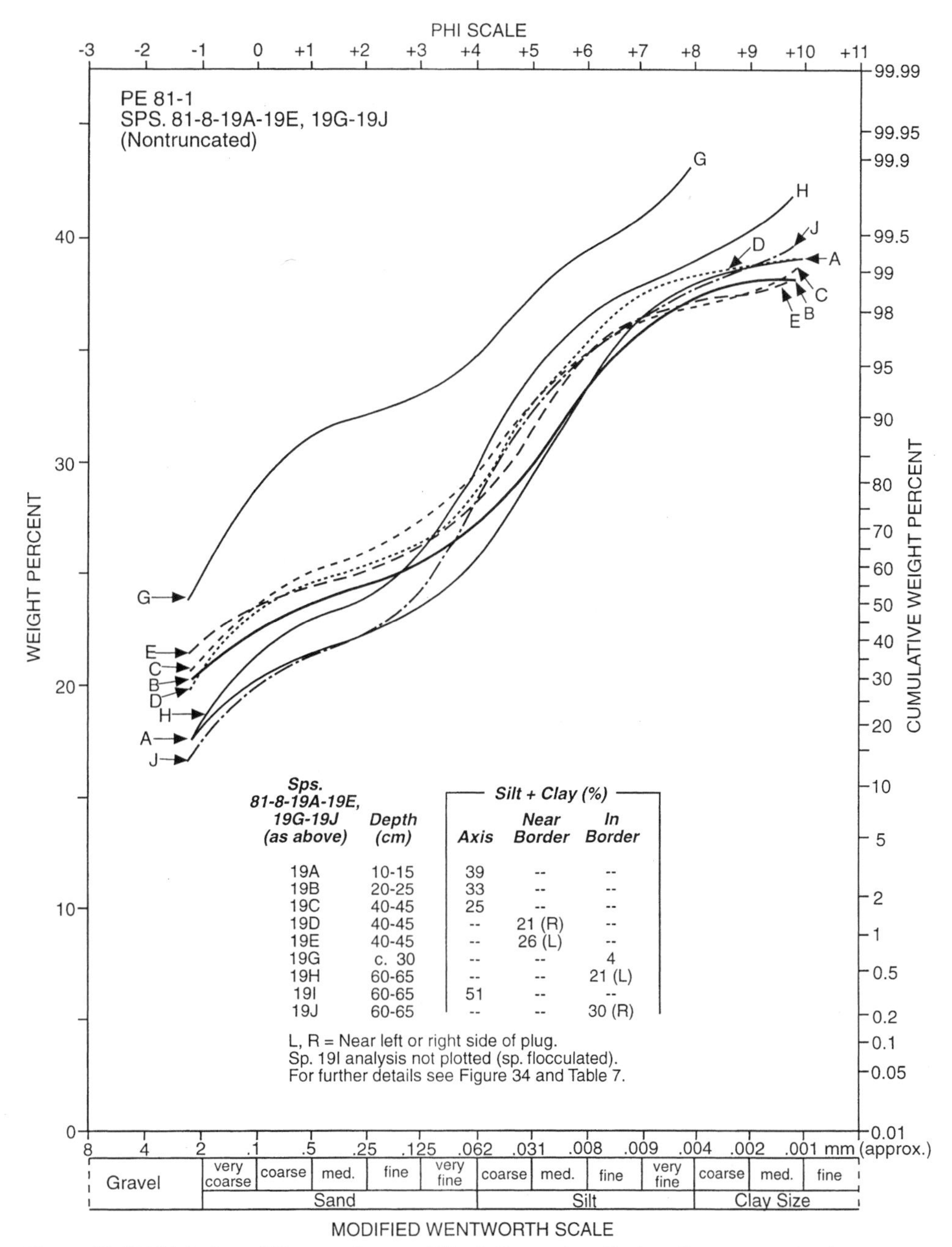

Figure 38. PE 81-1 about 350 m southwest of North Transmitter Station. Summary grain-size analyses of specimens in Figure 37.

neck rested in a thaw basin. Most of the water collecting in the basin (which had to be periodically bailed) seemed to issue from thawing of stony fines rather than from the gravel.

Two other nearby plug excavations showed the same combination of features—a concentration of fines in the top few centimeters of a plug, a thaw basin, a subsurface upslope neck, and slabby clasts in a plug tending to be on edge with long axis vertical. Most of the plug circles in the area were characterized on their upslope side by an irregular plug pit associated with larger stones than those bordering other sectors of a plug.

PE 83-3. Several excavations were made on a prominent bedrock bench near the northwest end of "Airport Ridge" (Fig. 3). In places the westward-facing bench front exposed slumped bedrock and was overlain to uncertain depths by unconsolidated sediments whose surface is close to the probable Holocene marine limit of 120 ± 3 m (see the section "General, Geography and geology"). On the west the bench surface exhibited pebbly carbonate stones, cobbles, and occasional small boulders. Some erratics were present, including crystalline rocks and reddish carbonates. The area was characterized by a mixture of weathered beachlike sediments, glacial sediments, and material derived from breakup of the underlying carbonate bedrock; on the east the tread merged with a prominent gelifluction slope.

PE 83-3 was on the bench where it inclined about 7° westerly. An area of 3 × 4.3 m was excavated in undisturbed gravel to a depth of 35 cm, some 5 cm below the frost table (8 September 1983). The excavation exhumed four plug S-circles, two plugs that had a subsurface relief up to 20 cm, and six small ridges. Three of the latter were definite plug necks, two connected to the upslope side and one to the downslope side of individual plugs (Fig. 39). The maximum exposed neck length was about 65 cm, and neck relief 15 cm. The largest circle measured 35 × 45 cm, with longest diameter trending downslope. The circles tended to have a more gentle downslope inclination than the general surface (ca. 2° versus 7°). The fines also tended to be more concentrated on the upslope than downslope side of the plugs (Table 14, Sps. 83-9-8A–8C). In general fines were also most prominent in the top 5 to 10 cm or so of a plug, decreasing with depth on the downslope side (Table 14, Sp. 83-9-8C), until the plugs merged with a stony diamicton. Scraping away loosely held plug gravel still in situ in 1986 left a pillar of fines-rich gravel inclined downslope.

Dye experiments

DE 86-3,-4. The following dye experiments were carried out on the south bank of McMaster River, north of ES C at estimated altitudes of some 18 to 20 m. Much of the slope material is probably of mixed origin—marine and/or glaciomarine and perhaps glacial. Several plug circles transitional to plug S-semicircles tended to be aligned along the contour and to merge with each other and develop small, irregular benchlike forms a few meters long parallel to the contour.

DE 86-3. Fluorescein dye solution was poured into gravel on a slope of 17° where the frost table was at a depth of 38 cm (29 July 1986). The insertion point lay 2 m upslope and 50 cm higher than a pit dug in coarse gravel at a marked depression along the inner edge of one of the small benchlike forms whose surface dipped slightly (4°) back into the slope. The frost table in the stony fines here lay at a depth of 60 cm. The dye appeared at the frost table in the pit in 40 sec, accompanied by a brownish thread of fines apparently carried from upslope along the frost table. A pit dug in a plug 5 m beyond and 1 m lower than the insertion point showed the dye when visited the next day, and the dye had also appeared in basal ice at the upper edge of a 17° snowbank and in basal ice at the foot of the snowbank 25 m lower than the insertion point.

DE 86-4. Dye was inserted into a 31° gravel slope, on the upslope side of a plug S-circle just above a small benchlike form near DE 86-3. The circle was 8.5 m upslope from the snowbank of DE 86-3. The dye, concentrated along the coarse borders of the plug S-circle and around the plug circles on the bench, appeared at the gravel frost table (depth 15 to 20 cm) half a meter upslope from the snowbank in 39 min, and eventually on the ice at the foot of the snowbank.

Figure 39. PE 83-3 near Northwest end of "Airport Ridge." View downslope. 15-cm rule in foreground lies on downslope side of small plug circle. In excavation, 30-cm rule on exhumed plug circle at right, 15-cm rule on small downslope plug at left (arrows point to rules).

Figure 40. Pluglike S-circle in larger N-pattern, east of VOR installation near north end of "Airport Ridge." 16-cm rule as scale.

Other observations

Vicinity VOR installation. An area slightly east of the VOR installation on "Airport Ridge" showed pluglike S-circles of relatively fine soil with a relief up to 7 cm occurring in larger nonsorted but somewhat stony patterns (Fig. 40).

Signal Hill plateau. Pluglike patterns occur on a 3 to 4° gradient near the top of the Signal Hill plateau slope toward the Mecham River. They were notable because of their convex central areas whose greatest relief was on their upslope side (Fig. 41), similar to the S-semicircles and slope-related forms in the vicinity of ES C and below the gravel haul road near the connection with the VOR road (see the section "Occurrences in Emerged Beach Gravel").

Higher on the plateau surface, at an altitude exceeding 175 m, which is well above the Holocene marine limit (120 ± 3 m; see the section "General, Geography and geology"), there is a striking northeast-southwest trend to a series of S-circles and S-nets, some pluglike (Fig. 42). This trend is roughly parallel to both the general gradient (7 to 8° in places) and to the strike of the Douro Formation on the west and the Cape Storm Formation on the east, the latter being the more dolomitic. Because of the dominantly circular to netlike pattern rather than normal stripelike pattern on a slope this steep, the primary trend control may be due to lithologic and structural differences in the bedrock as reflected in soil conditions—this despite the fact that the general surface here lacks bedrock exposures.

OCCURRENCES IN DISINTEGRATING BEDROCK

Excavations

PE 82-4. A number of plug S-circles occur amid disintegrating dolomite bedrock at an altitude of about 73 m some 50 m south of PE 81-1 (see the section "Occurrences in Miscellaneous Deposits"), southwest of the North Transmitter Station. Surface conditions were similar to those at PE 81-1 but easterly, steeply dipping, disintegrating bedrock was at the surface in the immediate vicinity of the excavation. The bedrock, slightly higher in the sequence than at PE 81-1, is slabby, including some very thin beds, and most of it is sufficiently fractured to be picked away by hand.

PE 82-4 was across a small plug circle of fines-rich gravel some 20 cm in diameter (Fig. 43). The frost table in the plug was at a depth of 23 cm upon initial excavation (30 June 1982). The plug was very stony, contained tiny (coarse, sand-size) shell fragments, and was surrounded by disintegrating bedrock whose clasts were up to small boulder size but commonly of pebble size. In places the clasts fitted together as in a mosaic

Figure 41. Pluglike S-circles and nets, Signal Hill plateau slope toward Mecham River northeast of top of Signal Hill. View downslope. Upslope side of features has prominent relief similar to plug S-semicircles. 16-cm rule at top of upslope side.

Figure 42. S-circles and nets, some pluglike; Signal Hill plateau near top. The features are aligned parallel to strike of carbonate bedrock. View downslope. 16-cm rule at left as scale (arrow points to rule).

Figure 43. Area of PE 82-4 about 450 m southwest of North Transmitter Station. View south along strike of disintegrating dolomitic bedrock. Circle shows plug S-circle of PE 82-4.

and were essentially in situ. The tiny shell fragments had infiltrated between some of the clasts, and small marble-size ice masses separated clasts around the plug at the base of the initial excavation. The fines of the plug circle appeared most concentrated in the top 5 cm. Continued excavation to a depth of 50 cm showed that the disintegrating bedrock overlay several small, fines-rich plugs at depth (Fig. 44).

PE 86-3. Plug excavation 86-3 was located north of the North Transmitter Station, on the south side of McMaster River just above its steep bank, whose top in the vicinity is at altitude of some 65 to 70 m. It was west of PE 82-1 (see the section "Occurrences in Miscellaneous Deposits") and along the strike of easterly dipping, disintegrating dolomite bedrock of the Allen Bay Formation with slightly varying lithology across the strike (Fig. 45). As at PE 82-4, plug circles and plugs were common. They ranged from low domes, reflecting underlying plugs in the disintegrating bedrock whose domed fragments tended to fit in mosaic fashion around a small plug circle of fines (Fig. 46), to forms where the mosaic aspect was present

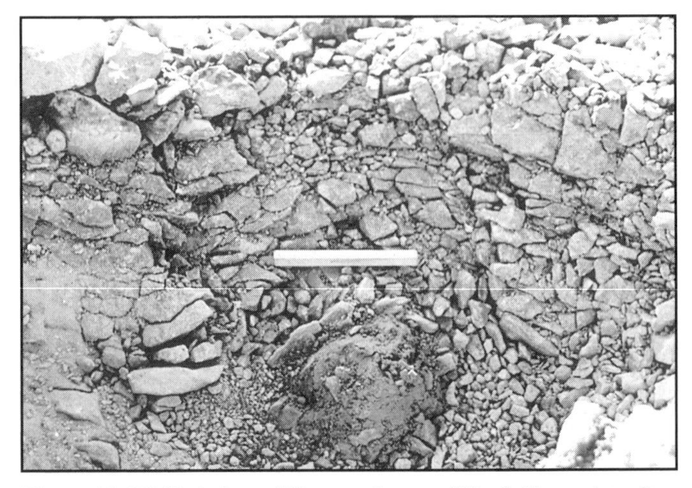

Figure 44. PE 82-4 about 450 m southwest of North Transmitter Station. In foreground, one of several small plugs that underlay the disintegrating bedrock surrounding plug S-circle in Figure 43. View west immediately downslope from Figure 43. Excavation depth 50 cm. 16-cm rule as scale at base of excavation.

but less apparent, to well-developed S-nets immediately to the west whose association with disintegrating bedrock was also present but not immediately obvious (Fig. 46, extreme right; cf. Fig. 57). The whole sequence appeared to be transitional beginning with plugs as discussed later in the section "Transitional Patterned-Ground Forms."

The circle of PE 86-3 measured 15 cm across and tended to be slightly mushroomlike in spreading out beyond its plug. The initial excavation was to the frost table at a depth of at least 26 cm in the stony fines of the plug but to 24 cm in the surrounding clasts (23 June 1986). At these depths, matching slabs were common beyond the plug, and in places fine material rested as a layer on top of a less fractured bedding surface (Fig. 47).

Figure 45. PE 86-3 about 350 m south of North Transmitter Station. View south toward North Transmitter Station along strike of disintegrating dolomite bedrock parallel to short ice axe handle (46-cm handle, 31-cm head). Surface slopes northwest. 15-cm rule (right of ice axe) shows position of PE 86-3, as also indicated by arrow.

Figure 46. PE 86-3 about 350 m south of North Transmitter Station, prior to excavation. View south. Short ice axe (46-cm handle, 31-cm head) and 15-cm rule in same position as in Figure 45.

Figure 48. PE 86-3. View west. 15-cm rule on circle top as scale. Depth of excavation 50 cm.

Excavation to a depth of 50 cm showed that the plug (Fig. 48), except for the top 7 cm where fines were at least slightly more concentrated, was very stony throughout, especially below 35 cm. Clasts were angular and in a matrix of fines. Many clasts were on edge, and their long axis tended toward the vertical if short and intermediate axes were similar. Fines and 1- to 2-cm clasts were present at the 50-cm depth, but larger fragments constituted the bulk of the plug.

The clasts surrounding the plug fitted together loosely and in many places had fractured in situ, with smaller fragments and fines separating some of the matching clasts (Fig. 49). A number of slabby clasts close to the plug were on edge more or less parallel to the plug but at slightly lesser angles. A few small (2 to 4 mm) shell fragments occurred to the maximum depth of excavation and demonstrated that fines would have been espe-

Figure 47. PE 86-3. View east. Depth of excavation 26 cm. Scale given by 15-cm rule (vertical against plug). 13-cm-long thermometer case in left foreground at base of excavation, and 14.5-cm-long pencil in right foreground. Thermometer lies on face of excavation at right. Note increasingly fine debris between large matching clasts near base of excavation.

Figure 49. PE 86-3. View north. 15-cm rule at upper right in same position as in Figure 48. Depth of excavation 50 cm. Note fine debris and disintegrating bedrock at left.

cially susceptible to downsifting to the permafrost table. Grain-size analyses are given in Table 15.

PE 88-1. Located at the crest of the first bedrock knob south of the VOR installation on "Airport Ridge," and thus above the Holocene marine limit, PE 88-1 was an example of a small rudimentary plug circle in disintegrating, slightly dolomitic limestone of the Douro Formation. Excavation to the frost table at a depth of 40 cm (5 July 1988) revealed a pluglike soil whose top 10 cm (Sp. 88-7-5D—truncated at 8 mm) was a clayey$_3$-silty$_{20}$-sandy$_{20}$ gravel$_{57}$ (M = clayey$_7$ silt$_{47}$-sand$_{47}$). The underlying central soil seemed similar, the whole irregularly encircled by the disintegrating bedrock, some fragments of which were in mosaic relationship to each other.

Other observations

Resolute area. A series of dolomitic bedrock ridges (Allen Bay Formation) striking roughly north-south crops out northeast of ES B between it and the North Transmitter Station road. Plug S-circles, some abutting each other, are well developed in the more-weathered beds, their appearance being very similar to the plug circles in the vicinity of PE 82-4.

Similar plug circles and plugs in disintegrating carbonate bedrock also occur at a number of other sites, including the benchlike, dolomitic ledges striking roughly north-south below an altitude of some 40 m along the west coast of Cornwallis Island opposite the southeast end of May Island and the dolomitic exposures about 200 m west of the PCSP complex. At the latter site some plug S-circles in disintegrating bedrock near the edge of a better-preserved bedrock exposure tended to merge some meters farther away with larger forms comprising S-nets and crudely developed RB S-circles in shell-bearing finer soil.

Sheringham Point. Plug S-circles in disintegrating carbonate bedrock are widespread at Sheringham Point in beds of the Upper Silurian, Cape Storm Formation, as at Resolute.

Gypsum diapir, west coast, Cornwallis Island. A gypsum diapir complex rises to a map altitude of between 500 and 600 ft at approximately latitude 75°10′N, longitude 96°15′W southeast of Stanley Head on the west coast of Cornwallis Island. On the west slope of the complex, disintegrating black shale bedrock (Cape Phillips Formation) domed by the diapir shows some striking pluglike circles (Fig. 50).

Mould Bay, Prince Patrick Island. A very brief visit to Mould Bay, Prince Patrick Island, permitted some comparative observations. The soils of the area have been described and mapped by Everett (1968, p. 11–39 and Plates I-III, p. 72–74).

Plug S-circles are common in places. Grain-size analysis of the top 15 cm or so of a high-relief plug form about half a kilometer north of the Mould Bay station showed the soil (Sp. 86-8-1A—truncated at 8 mm) to be a clayey$_2$-gravelly$_{14}$-silty$_{21}$ sand$_{63}$ (M = clayey$_2$-silty$_{24}$ sand$_{74}$). About the same distance northwest of the station, plug S-circles were common in disintegrating sandstone bedrock, and in places they seemed responsible for the surface disruption of extensive areas. The need to catch the return flight to Resolute Bay left no time for excavations.

Figure 50. Plug S-circle in black shale (Cape Phillips Formation), west slope gypsum diapir about 8 km southeast of Stanley Head, west coast, Cornwallis Island. Short ice axe (46-cm handle, 31-cm head) as scale.

MISCELLANEOUS OBSERVATIONS

Recent activity

Fresh-appearing S-circle activity was noted in a number of places, one of which permitted dating. Sometime during the 1950–1960 period, and again in 1966, bare copper wires were buried in radiating, ploughlike furrows at several sites around the North Transmitter Station to improve VLF (very low frequency) grounding characteristics (Fig. 51). Since then, the circles have disrupted the furrows, the circles being commonly better developed, larger, and more frequent along the earlier wire lines (Fig. 52) than the later. All the views were within the

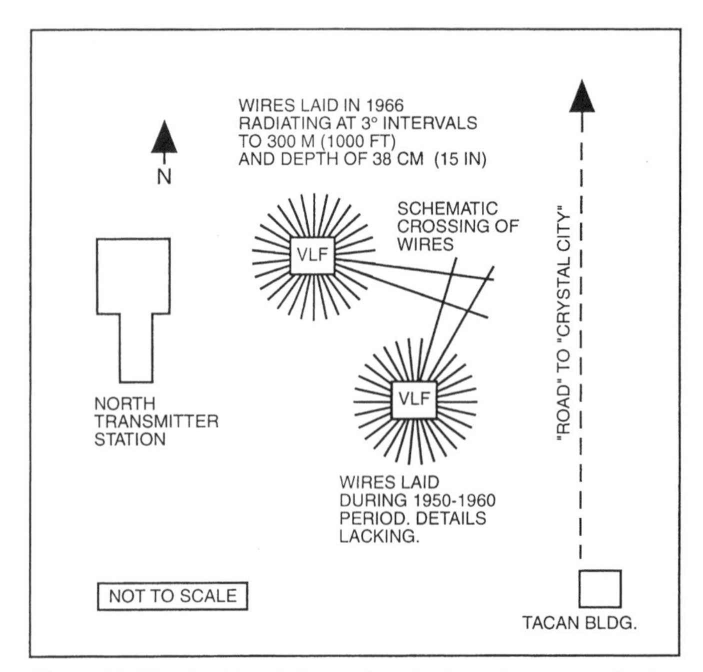

Figure 51. Sketch of North Transmitter Station VLF groundwire layout. Courtesy Ron Lupack, Station Chief, June 1988.

Figure 52. Plug S-circles along a VLF groundwire line from pre-1966 high-voltage shed. View northeast. 15-cm rule on a circle.

area of crossing wire lines in Figure 51. The dome-shaped and even-bordered nature of some of the forms and their surface similarity to excavated plug S-circles left little doubt that they continued to depth as plugs.

Recent plug activity was also apparent in bulldozed areas, along with frost-action effects such as edgewise projecting stones and miniature sorted patterns, but the dates of bulldozing could not be established.

Terrain influences

Earlier discussions cited the tendency for plug S-circles, plug S-semicircles, and associated plugs to be aligned in rows more or less parallel to the contour in some areas of emerged beach gravels, especially where there were marked decreases in slope, as was true of many of the Resolute plug S-circles, as above ES C (Fig. 27), in the vicinity of PE 89-2 below the gravel haul road, and at "Summit Lake" near the top of Sheringham Point. At the latter site the slope bordering the lake on the south is very slight and is essentially free of circles despite at least seasonally saturated conditions. On the north side, however, plug S-circles with shell fragments are abundant below an abrupt and steep rise culminating in the bedrock top of the Point. Seepage here was probably the critical site factor contributing to the location of these circles.

The rise of clay-size particles in a decapitated plug at Resolute was observed by Cook (1956, p. 16), who cited capillarity as the cause. Rise of water with dye in a decapitated plug was noted at ES C during the present investigation, and seepage may have been involved, as was clearly the case below ES C where fines issued from along the frost table when the surface was being cut back a few centimeters.

Also instructive was a series of well-developed plug S-circles that were aligned downslope on a variable 4 to 8° gradient east of the VOR installation on "Airport Ridge" (Fig. 53). The plugs had brought relatively coarse subsurface gravel to the surface, as was the case on the north side of PE 86-6 at ES C (Fig. 21) and at a number of other places. The downslope alignment of the plugs shown in Figure 53 and their transfer of soil to the surface strongly favored the role of seepage in localizing the plugs.

Figure 53. Plug S-circles aligned downslope, east of VOR installation near north end "Airport Ridge." 16-cm rule as scale. Shovel oriented along fall line.

These distributions strongly suggest the importance of topographically controlled hydrologic conditions and seepage in influencing the growth of plugs. Snow patches during the thaw season can contribute significantly to seepage, both immediately upslope of the patches by thinning the active layer and concentrating subsurface flow and downslope by being a continuing source of thaw water as noted by Egginton (1979, p. 353). The hydraulic effects of variations in the active layer at Resolute are discussed in some detail by Woo and Steer (1983) and Woo and Xia (1995, 1996).

Weathering

As discussed earlier in the section "Occurrences in Disintegrating Bedrock," the development of plug S-circles and associated plugs in weathering bedrock is commonly documented by their association with a mosaic of rock fragments whose arrangement reflects the bedrock structure (Fig. 49). Such assemblages, as well as mosaics of rock fragments that are not in an obvious in-situ bedrock relationship, are far more common than might first be supposed, becoming apparent when looked for carefully.

Another common mosaic feature was an initial decrease in size of rock fragments with depth from the surface, whether or not the mosaic relationship was in disintegrating bedrock. In some cases as at PE 86-3 (see the section "Occurrences in Disintegrating Bedrock"), continuity with bedrock was probable, although the contact with solid bedrock here was not observed; presumably the fragment size increased again, since both physical and chemical weathering would tend to decrease with depth near unaffected bedrock. Even given comparable lithology and structure, an explanation for the presence of larger mosaic clasts at the surface than just below it becomes rather speculative. Perhaps their presence is related to sudden and large rock-surface temperature changes in polar environments and/or the presence of more persistent moisture at depth than at the surface. The effect of large rock-surface temperature changes has been mostly restricted to spalling effects (cf. Eichler, 1981, p. 460–463), but polygonal cracks are not necessarily excluded (Hall and Hall, 1991, p. 108). Increased weathering of rocks at depth because of persistent moisture was argued long ago (Elton, 1927, p. 184–192; Huxley and Odell, 1924, p. 219–224) in connection with S-circles and has been recently cited in connection with generation of fines near the permafrost table (Hallet et al., 1991, p. 295). As emphasized by Hall (1991), the interrelation of different mechanical weathering processes in a geocryological context is complex.

Probably much of the surface debris represents in-situ disintegration of the carbonate bedrock and of locally derived or transported clasts, with the subsequent disruption of the mosaics by frost action and slope processes. Much of the plateau soil, which is rich in sand, silt, and clay particles at altitudes above the Holocene marine limit (120 ± 3 m; see the section "General, Geography and geology") and especially above 150 to 200 m, may include fine material that originated more or less in situ, as suggested by Cruickshank (1971, p. 197–198, 208), although he also indicated the possibility of an eolian origin. Although concurring that wind has probably contributed to some deposits, I believe that the strong relation in lithology and structural trend between the underlying bedrock and the overlying deposit demonstrates the importance of in-situ weathering. Nevertheless, where deposits include Pleistocene shells or shell fragments, they presumably also include some previously weathered material, whether strictly local or transported by glacial or other processes.

TRANSITIONAL PATTERNED-GROUND FORMS

Resolute area

As cited in the section "Earlier Observations," Mackay (1953, p. 86) noted that "Individual plugs may eventually lose their identities as they merge to form other types of patterned ground." Although details were lacking, this was a perceptive observation, confirmed by the present study.

Transitional diameters of plug S-circles were common in well-developed beach debris as noted earlier, a common range being from barely perceptible surface expressions to diameters of some 50 cm, although the absolute range is considerably greater. Several plug S-circles in the vicinity of ES B have a diameter of about 1 m.

Transitional pattern types occur in a number of places, including some lacking a well-developed mantle of beach debris.

Bench near northwest end of "Airport Ridge." As described earlier in connection with PE 83-3 (see the section "Occurrences in Miscellaneous Deposits"), the bench is characterized at its northwest end by fines-rich gravel and slabby rock fragments of various sizes, with many of the fragments, obviously derived from the underlying dolomitic bedrock of the bench, disintegrating in situ. Sorted-net patterns dominated, and contiguous but otherwise typical plug S-circles were present and appeared to be transitional to the S-nets. The entire area gave the impression of being patterned by plug activity.

Vicinity ES B. Transitional patterns were noted in traversing west from the plugs in the disintegrating dolomite bedrock northeast of ES B, through pluglike, S-net patterns to larger S-nets and elongate forms on a 2.0 to 2.5° slope, then south to ES B on a 1.0 to 1.5° slope along the shore of a small shallow lake where well-developed RB S-circles with borders 5 to 10 cm high occur in places (Fig. 54; see Washburn, 1989, p. 941–944). Several typical plug circles were noted less than 10 m upslope of an RB S-circle. Except for the RB S-circles here, the forms appeared to represent a series starting from undoubted plug circles. There were also transitions in the ES B area from several EB S-circles to the RB S-circle type.

S-Circle Excavation 88-A and vicinity. S-Circle Excavation 88-A was at an altitude of about 83 m, some 100 m equidistant from the VOR road and the gravel haul road toward

Figure 54. RB S-circles, Experimental Site B. Circle in foreground about 2.5 m in diameter. View north.

Figure 56. S-Circle Excavation 88-A, about 100 m north of VOR road and west of gravel haul road toward TACAN Building. View northwest. 1-m stick and 15-cm rule as scales.(Cf. Fig. 55.)

the TACAN building. The excavation illustrated a circle that seemed transitional from plug forms to RB S-circles. The circle (Figs. 55, 56) had a central area with minimum/maximum diameters of 155 and 180 cm and was thus appreciably larger than most plug S-circles in the Resolute area. Its border was somewhat ringlike in places but not high enough (5 cm) to denote the circle as an RB S-circle. Several adjacent circles were of generally similar appearance, with diameters of 110 and 110 cm, 140 and 150 cm, and 190 and 205 cm.

Depth to the frost table established by probing the central area of Excavation 88-A was 62 cm (18 July 1988). Water rose to within 35 cm of the surface soon after excavating was started, and it had to be discontinued. Excavating was resumed on 1 September and extended to a depth of 50 cm. The former bottom of the excavation had frozen but not deeply, and water to a depth of 5 cm soon accumulated during digging and collecting of specimens.

Figure 55. S-Circle Excavation 88-A, about 100 m north of VOR road and west of gravel haul road toward TACAN Building. View northeast prior to excavation. 15-cm rule in foreground, 1-m stick across northeast side.

Some features of the excavation are illustrated in Figure 56, and grain-size analyses are given in Table 16. Overall, for specimens truncated at 8 mm, the central soil from a depth of 5 cm (below a more gravelly surface) to 50 cm was predominantly a clayey-silty-gravelly sand with clay ranging from 2 to 10% and silt from 13 to 24%. The northwest face of Excavation 88-A showed irregular ice lenses up to 4 mm thick; ice amid granules was up to 6 mm in diameter with vertical bubble zones more pronounced than in the irregular lenses. The northeast and southeast faces exhibited coarse, openwork border gravel, but the coarse gravel in the southeast face was underlain by fines, as was the southwest face.

Nearby, the surface of the similar S-circles showed that some places in the central areas had more fines than others and were of slightly different color, as if the fines had recently emerged as distinct small circles within the larger circle. Probing in one of the circles gave a frost-table depth of 59 cm after hammering the probe through a frozen layer. Similar probing in another circle was slightly deeper but less than 65 cm on the same date (1 September 1988), and the bottom of the probe froze in so quickly it could not be withdrawn. Comparison with the 62-cm depth of the frost table on 18 July, before the latter had probably reached its maximum depth, suggests that upfreezing from the permafrost table was well under way.

The circles in the area were ideally circular rather than netlike or suggestive of a possible crack origin with subsequent expansion and mutual accommodation. Some circles were domed and had radial and concentric cracks developed by dilation during heaving and/or contraction following doming. The rather ringlike nature of the forms, their somewhat varied size, and the nearby presence of plugs and plug circles suggest the occurrence of closely related forms and a transition from plug

S-circles to somewhat ringlike S-circles that, with higher borders, would be RB S-circles.

Vicinity North Transmitter Station. PE 86-3 north of the North Transmitter Station exhumed one of several plugs in disintegrating bedrock, as previously described. The slightly lower area a few meters to the west was characterized by well-developed S-nets (Fig. 45, extreme right; Fig. 57). The bordering stones, which included cobbles and isolated boulders, were largely derived from underlying dolomite of the Allen Bay Formation (Fig. 4) as revealed by slight variations in color and lithology parallel to the strike of nearby bedrock. Minimum and maximum diameters of the well-developed nets included, for the central fines-rich gravel, 15 and 20 cm, 50 and 50 cm, and 55 and 70 cm with longest dimension being along a 3 to 4° northward slope toward the steep river bank. The accompanying stony borders were commonly about 20 cm wide, forming depressions above which the best-developed central areas rose about 15 cm. Many clasts in the borders interlocked in detail, not only in a planar array but also three dimensionally, and were obviously weathering in situ and not circulating to depth. Smaller clasts occurred beneath the coarser ones. Shell fragments were present in the central areas but scarce. Some central areas showed much less weathering of clasts and fresher-appearing fines than at the borders. Some of the comparatively fresh clasts were lithologically slightly different than the bordering clasts and were probably from a lower-lying horizon. The whole aspect was that of a flowering of the bedrock and an assemblage of contiguous plug S-circles in a transitional sequence to plug S-nets starting with forms obviously originating in extensively fractured bedrock.

Southeast of the North Transmitter Station a ridge with the "road" to "Crystal City" at its crest descends eastward to an emerged cove that opens northward to a swale containing a small pond. The north and east sides of this ridge show a sequence of sorted patterns from hillside plug S-circles to pluglike forms transitional to S-circles with somewhat ringlike stony borders (Fig. 58), and then to fully developed RB S-circles (Fig. 59) on a transect from high ground to the swale, where the RB S-circles lie adjacent to the pond. Also in the swale were vague transitions between S-nets and S-polygons. In a number of the central areas there were small fresh-appearing patches of soil, characterized by a difference in color or grain size, as if they were small plug N-circles contributing to development of the larger circles and nets.

Vicinity TACAN building. The area east and southeast of the TACAN building has a number of rises and swales with sorted patterns. An almost closed depression on the east (just south of a rise overlooking a small lake) exhibited typical plug S-circles in stony soil on the westerly (i.e., east-facing) slope. The underlying carbonate bedrock is dolomitic and probably part of the Cape Storm Formation. The circles range in size from barely perceptible to a form with minimum/maximum diameters of 50 and 70 cm, giving way toward the center of the depression to larger convex, circular to netlike sorted patterns. These larger patterns varied from perfectly circular with a

Figure 58. Pluglike forms (lower left) transitional to RB S-circles, swale with pond east of "road" to "Crystal City." 15-cm rule below largest circle as scale.

Figure 57. Pluglike S-net area north of North Transmitter Station. View south to station. 15-cm rule in foreground (at right of snow remnant; arrow points to rule) and person as scales.

Figure 59. RB S-circles adjacent to pond, swale east of "road" to "Crystal City." 15-cm rule at center of circle in foreground as scale.

diameter of 160 cm to a more irregularly circular form with minimum/maximum diameters of 192 and 238 cm. Two perfectly circular merging forms, tending toward a figure-eight pattern (cf. Cook, 1958, his Fig. 2), had respective diameters of 82 and 155 cm (Fig. 60), the smaller having the aspect of a typical pluglike S-circle. Excavation of a common border between two other circles showed small stones at the surface along one sector of the border and slabby dolomitic limestone clasts along a contiguous sector. Flat-lying tabular cobble sizes in the latter sector overlay finer soil at an estimated depth of 15 to 20 cm, and matching border clasts indicated that much of the slabby border debris had disintegrated in situ, with perhaps some of the underlying finer debris being related weathering products.

Several of the larger sorted patterns contained smaller ones, some relatively fresh and similar to plug S-circles in being dominantly circular and convex. The smaller plug circles upslope and the generally larger sorted patterns in the depression may be simply transitional forms of comparable origin, the development of the larger being favored by the presence of abundant fines from upslope and by the generally wet environment downslope. In any event, the presence of transitional forms is clearly indicated.

Vicinity VOR installation. South of the VOR installation on "Airport Ridge" and well above the Holocene marine limit, small N-nets adjoin a more stony area with the appearance of typical plug S-circles. The central areas of the circles were some 40 cm across, similar to the dimensions of the N-nets (Fig. 61). The transition between the patterns was clearly controlled by the stoniness of the surface.

Plateau above Small Lake. The slope immediately east of Small Lake rises abruptly to a plateau at an altitude of about 80 m. Circles, including a small figure-eight combination of two circles that appeared to be intermediate between EB S-circles and RB S-circles, were noted on a bench some 12 m below the plateau (Fig. 62). An excellently developed figure-eight combination from the vicinity of Resolute Bay was described by Cook (1958). On the plateau itself, south of the southernmost of several small lakes, there were transitions from plug tops just below the general gravel surface, to typical EB plug S-circles, to some small but well-developed circles with stony borders approaching the RB type (Fig. 63). A nearby conical 7-cm-deep pit in the gravel surface was similar to some plug pits of the Taylor River Bend site described next, and possibly of the same origin.

Figure 60. S-circles, central area of almost-closed depression east of TACAN Building. Pluglike S-circle in left foreground merging with RB S-circle, right foreground. 16-cm rule on latter as scale.

Figure 61. Plug S-circles at right merging with N-nets at left, south of VOR installation near north end "Airport Ridge." 16-cm rule as scale.

Taylor River bend

The Taylor River, which drains much of southwest Cornwallis Island, has a prominent bend upstream to the north—"Taylor River bend"—near latitude 74°45′N; longitude 95°10′W. About 3 km east of here on the south side of the junction of Taylor River with a tributary from the east, there is a rather flat-topped, elongate low hill about 15 m high, measuring about 1 km northwest-southeast and up to 0.75 km across. Vegetation is largely lacking. At the crest of the hill the surface consists mainly of sand and gravel except where slumping exposed underlying silt.[7] Permafrost cracks are prominent in places. The surface of the lower slopes consists of silty sand and gravel with interspersed more-silty areas.

Examination of the lower east and southeast slopes revealed a number of S-circles and S-nets, especially near wet swales, and an instructive variety of plug circles over much of the area. Small RB S-circles were present in places. In one instance (Fig. 64), the domed area, presumably due to an underlying plug, was in a partially ring-bordered circle that was tending toward a figure-eight pattern. The inferred plug had raised a bulge in the central area of the circle. Probably another plug had begun to intrude the far stony border (by ice axe in the figure) as shown by a difference in gravel color.

In several locations a sequence of plug forms could be traced downslope beginning with forms underlying domed

Figure 62. Figure-8 combination of two small circles intermediate between EB S-circles and RB S-circles, bench some 12 m below plateau above Small Lake (Fig. 3). 15-cm rule as scale (lengthwise along junction of larger circle on right with smaller, poorly developed circle on left; arrow points to rule).

gravel (Fig. 65) to small plug S-circles with somewhat ring-like borders (Fig. 66), to plug or stony pits, the latter being a pit whose bottom shows mainly openwork gravel (Fig. 67).[8] A spot check of deep pits as such showed that of six pits exposing plug soil, the average depth was 6 cm (range 4 to 9 cm); of eight stony pits, the average depth was twice as much (12 cm; range 10–14 cm). Excavation then auguring to the frost table at a depth of 71 cm (19 August 1987) showed sandy fines underlying a stony pit. That these pits were probably due to plug collapse, rather than being indicative of ascending plugs as suggested by Mackay (1953, p. 35) for occurrences at Resolute, was indicated by the bordering concentration of coarse gravel, in this case probably raised from depth by a plug and left at the surface as a precollapse plug-circle border.

The above sequence strongly suggests an evolution of forms consequent on growth of plugs (Fig. 65), their exposure at the surface as plug circles (Fig. 66), followed by collapse as the result of thawing of ice concentrations within or at the base of the plugs (Fig. 67). That plugs can collapse from thawing was demonstrated by the development of depressions centered on plugs decapitated by recent bulldozing near the Resolute TACAN building.

Near a wet swale where S-circles and S-nets were prominent but not of themselves clearly plug forms, there appeared to be transitions between typical plug circles and these sorted forms.

Figure 63. Transitions from plug S-circles to circles approaching RB S-circles (foreground), plateau above Small Lake (Fig. 3). View northerly. 15-cm rule as scale.

Lake 2 km north of Helen Haven

An instructive series of sorted circles was observed on the east shore of a small lake at an altitude between 90 and 120 m at latitude 77°19′N, longitude 93°43′W about 2 km north of Helen Haven on the east coast of Cornwallis Island (Canada National Topographic System Map 58G [Baillie–Hamilton Island], scale 1:250,000). A gravel flat at the lake outlet showed

Figure 64. RB S-circle with dome over inferred plug, easterly slope of elongate hill south of Taylor River tributary about 3 km east of "Taylor River bend," interior Cornwallis Island. 15-cm rule on dome (diameter of dome 65 cm, relief 4.5 cm.). Short ice ace (46-cm handle, 31-cm head) lies on gravelly border 40 to 50 cm wide, 10 cm high).

Figure 66. Plug circles with somewhat ringlike stony borders in foreground, and stony pit and plug pits in background beyond short ice axe, easterly slope of elongate hill south of Taylor River tributary about 3 km east of "Taylor River bend," interior Cornwallis Island. View downslope. Scale given by short ice axe (46-cm handle, 31-cm head) in background. (Cf. Fig. 67.)

Figure 65. Domed gravel over a plug, easterly slope of elongate hill south of Taylor River tributary about 3 km east of "Taylor River bend," interior Cornwallis Island. Scale given by short ice axe (46-cm handle, 31-cm head).

all gradations from isolated pluglike S-circles (Fig. 68) to nearly adjoining circles with somewhat ringlike stony borders in places. It was obvious from the isolated circles in uniform stretches of unpatterned ground that the circles originated by fines at depth breaking through a gravel cover as opposed to stones being radially sorted from stony soil. An early stage of this process was described in connection with PE 86-6 (see the section "Occurrences in Emerged Beach Gravel").

CHARACTERISTICS OF PLUGS AND PLUG CIRCLES

General

Characteristics of plugs and plug circles, described with minimal interpretation in the preceding sections, are summarized here. A wider-ranging, more interpretative discussion, including observations from elsewhere, is presented as a prelude to considering hypotheses of origin.

Figure 67. Stony pits and plug pits, easterly slope of elongate hill south of Taylor River tributary about 3 km east of "Taylor River bend," interior Cornwallis Island. View downslope of same three pits shown beyond ice axe in background of Figure 66. Scale given by short ice axe (46-cm handle, 31-cm head).

Figure 68. Nearly adjoining S-circles with suggestions of borders rising above central areas, east shore small lake about 2 km north of Helen Haven, east coast Cornwallis Island. Person as scale.

Constitution: Review

1. Plugs and their surface expression as plug circles range in constitution from fines to diamictons, with stones predominating overall and fines in the matrix.

2. Plug circles are surrounded by soil of different character—an openwork gravel in the case of many sorted forms.

3. The plug soil can be dominantly a marine deposit, a sediment of mixed origin, or weathered bedrock.

4. Plug fines tend to be laterally most widespread (not necessarily most concentrated) near the base of plugs (PE 90-1, Fig. 29) and near the ground surface (PE 90-1, Fig. 30) (see the section "Occurrences in Emerged Beach Gravel"). In part the locations reflect, respectively, the immediate source of a plug and the near-surface, downslope stretching out and thinning of plug soil.

5. In places plug fines tend to be most concentrated on the upslope side of plug circles, as noted by Egginton (1972) (see the section "Earlier Observations"). This concentration may be explained by the fact that plug soil near the surface stretches out downslope (see 4 above) and is replaced on the upslope side by heaving of relatively "fresh" plug soil from depth as at PE 89-2 (Fig. 25) (see the section "Occurrences in Emerged Beach Gravel").

6. Cook (1956, p. 16) observed that where a plug had been decapitated, water milky with suspended clay issued from it. "By the end of the summer there was a noticeable concentration of fines at the surface where the original plug had been beheaded." He inferred that capillary flow had brought the fines. I have also observed water oozing from decapitated plugs.

7. Subsurface fines can be carried downslope by water moving along the frost table as it lowers during thawing, as observed in the Resolute area where seepage was bringing fines to the surface below ES C.

Constitution: Discussion

1. In addition to being derived from a preexisting underlying bed, the fines in plugs can be from various other sources.

   a. In-situ weathering was discussed in relation to patterned ground many years ago (Nansen, 1922, p. 111–120; Huxley and Odell, 1924, p. 219–224; and Elton, 1927, p. 184–192). In the Resolute plugs, material partly derived from in-situ weathering of adjacent coarse material is probably represented by small angular fragments and fines between matching clasts of disintegrating bedrock. Where dolomite or dolomitic debris is common, as in the Resolute area, silt production is promoted by solution of calcite cement in the parent material. The accumulation of residual silt by in-situ weathering of carbonate rocks in Spitsbergen was discussed by Etzelmüller and Sollid (1991, p. 186–190) and Mann et al. (1986), among others, supplemented by laboratory experiments and further considerations

(Sletten, 1993). Additional references are included below in citing translocation of residual silt.

b. The effect of frost action in breaking soil particles was reported by Sumgin (1931, p. 14) and Corte (1961, p. 6); its grinding effect in increasing the content of fines in soils was also cited by Rieger (1983, p. 31–32) but details are lacking.

2. Corte (1962a, p. 8–9, 19) explained concentrations of fines (grain diameter <0.074 mm, 200 ASA mesh in the engineering usage he adopted; Corte, 1962b, p. 4) in the active layer by exclusion of the fines ahead of a downward and laterally moving freezing front, combined with the effect of gravity. He contrasted this kind of "vertical and horizontal sorting" with "mechanical sorting" whereby overlying unfrozen soil is mechanically disturbed by "bottom-up" freezing from the permafrost table, again leading to downward movement of fines by gravity but otherwise being the inverse of sorting by migration of fines ahead of a freezing front. Corte (1962b, p. 72) also noted that accumulation of fines at the permafrost table might be the result of downwashing but that definite conclusions required more laboratory work, although such accumulations could then become subject to upward movement by differences in density or thermal properties. Microscale frost-heaving experiments by Corte (1972) showed that upward progress of fines accompanied progressive heaving.

The difference between such downwashing and accumulation (illuviation) of fines at depth and migration of fines to depth ahead of a freezing front might be difficult to distinguish in the field.

3. Downward concentration of fines in the active layer by illuviation is a common process. Coarse silt (0.02 to 0.05 mm) as well as fine silt (<0.02 mm) can move downward through medium sand (0.25 to 0.5 mm) and fine silt also through fine sand (0.10 to 0.25 mm), according to laboratory experiments (Wright and Foss, 1968). At Resolute the downward sifting of coarse, sand-size shell fragments was noted at PE 82-4 (see the section "Occurrences in Disintegrating Bedrock"). Illuviation of fines (including windborne fines) by drainage of rain and thaw water as the frost table lowers was discussed by Kreida (1959, p. 52, 55), who referred to the downward movement of clay fractions (<0.002 mm) from upper soil horizons, their increase at the permafrost table, and the opposing effect of their subsequent frost heaving toward the surface. Corte (1962b, p. 72) cited the possibility of downwashing of fines to the permafrost table in Greenland; Jania (1977, p. 112) and Forman and Miller (1984, p. 386–391) were impressed by the evidence for it in Spitsbergen, as were Locke (1986) in Baffin Island, and Tedrow and Krug (1982) at Bathurst Island (west of Cornwallis Island). The origin and subsurface movement of fines in Spitsbergen was repeatedly discussed by Büdel (1961, p. 352–353, 360, 365; 1977, p. 56–57; 1982, p. 76–77; 1987, p. 61–63, 81–84); it was also cited by Etzelmüller and Sollid (1991, p. 189), Herz and Andreas (1966, p. 193–197), and Semmel (1969, p. 48–49). The importance here of translocated silt in the origin of sorted circles was stressed by Van Vliet-Lanoë (1983, p. 9, 11; 1988a, p. 419; 1988b, p. 90–91; 1988c, p. 1011; 1989a).

4. The downward concentrations of fines in the active layer by frost heaving ("jacking") of stones, leaving voids that become filled with finer soil during thawing, is widely accepted. The result is an upward displacement of stones, the eventual ejection of some at the surface, and a relative increase in concentrations of fines at depth as recognized by Corte (1962a, p. 8, his Fig. 9) and many others and reviewed elsewhere (Washburn, 1979, p. 80–89).

5. An upward movement of fines as water is drawn to an evaporating surface was mentioned by Johansson (1914, p. 19–20, 22), reported in laboratory experiments by Brewer and Haldane (1957, p. 303, 308), and inferred by Cook (1956, p. 16) as cited above under "Constitution: Review, 6." Perhaps movement of water to a freezing front could also carry fines, as independently suggested by Bernard Hallet (personal communication, 1987) and Washburn (1956, p. 841). All these processes might contribute to plugs becoming enriched in fines, but the processes require further research, and their quantitative importance remains to be demonstrated.

6. Silt translocation in an alpine environment (Colorado Front Range) was discussed by Dixon (1986, p. 147–148, 155). However, despite the importance of the subject, quantitative data on the origin and subsurface translocation of fines in periglacial environments are still largely lacking. Pertinent references from nonpermafrost environments include Imeson et al. (1984, p. 223).

7. Whatever the source of fines in a plug, it should be noted that plugs can become a focus of accelerated weathering, both physical and chemical, and thus for generation of more fines and hence more ice lensing and heaving.

8. A plug can give rise to coarser as well as finer soil at the surface, as described from the north side of PE 86-6 at ES C. The result is analogous to that cited by Jahn (1963, p. 144, his Fig. 16), although he interpreted the soil as having been originally sorted by frost action rather than being a normal sedimentary bed as appeared to be the case at ES C.

Morphology, structure, and fabric: Review

1. Individual plugs can either be cylindrical or have the shape of a blunt cone or more irregular shape tapering upward. They can be pinnacles on a plug ridge or be upward projections from a more widespread subsurface horizon.

2. The long axis of elongate stones in plugs tends to be steeply inclined or vertical.

3. Plugs in beach gravel can have bordering stones tightly packed along their sides or more loosely held. In either case tabular stones tend to be on edge so that a flat surface parallels plug sides.

4. Many plug circles in beach gravel have a slight depression on their upslope side. Conical pits (plug pits) occur over some plug tops (see the section "Morphology, structure, and fab-

ric: Discussion, 3," below), and in at least some places the pits are probably of thermokarst origin as discussed in the section "Transitional Patterned-Ground Forms, Taylor River bend."

Morphology, structure, and fabric: Discussion

1. Plugs in beach gravel originate at depth. This is shown by (1) their structure (including fabric); (2) soil and shells from depth; (3) doming of overlying surface material, including disintegrating bedrock; and (4) their exposure at the surface as plug circles. Similar occurrences of comparatively fine centers emerging through a preexisting stony surface layer (as opposed, for instance, to being the result of radial sorting of stones from a stony central area of finer soil) was suggested by Hamberg (1915, p. 595–596) and has been repeatedly described (Büdel, 1960, p. 47–60; Büdel, 1987, p. 54–60 in modified form; Cegła, 1973, p. 239; Chambers, 1967, p. 20; Elton, 1927, p. 186–187; Jahn, 1963, p. 144; Schunke, 1975, p. 122; and others, including recently Etzelmüller and Sollid, 1991, p. 189–190, their Fig. 8; Sollid and Sørbel, 1988, p. 58–60; and Van Vliet-Lanoë, 1988a, p. 418–420; Van Vliet-Lanoë, 1988b, p. 90–92).

2. Rise of plugs could be promoted over time by
   a. Differential frost heaving.
   b. Development of vesicles in plug fines, as observed for instance at PE 81-1, since presumably some vesicles would be preserved during thaw collapse and the process would be repetitive, with additional fines becoming available for vesicle development as in 2c and 2d (see also the section "Constitution: Discussion, 1–7").
   c. Physical weathering of larger rock particles in a plug into smaller, more numerous, and more space-consuming particles.
   d. Surfaceward movement involving differing bulk densities or presence of sufficiently strong hydraulic gradient.

3. The origin of plug pits and less pronounced depressions on the upslope side of some plugs (see the section "Morphology, structure, and fabric: Review, 4") requires explanation.
   a. Some plugs lean slightly downslope, which might lead to collapse of material on the upslope side. However, many plugs show no such lean, yet have an upslope depression.
   b. The general nature of a plug itself leading to its rising above the general surface on the upslope side but becoming subject to mass-wasting on the downslope side would also be applicable here as well as to the plug semicircles at PE 89-2 (see the section "Occurrences in Emerged Beach Gravel").
   c. Perhaps downslope flow of water against a plug during freezing causes ice lensing, followed by collapse, with loosening of the soil leading to downslope removal of some soil particles, as suggested by Bernard Hallet (personal communication, 1994).
   d. The origin of truly conical plug pits on the upslope side of some plugs is probably a different question. Mackay (1953, p. 35) thought that the conical pits he observed, which were from some centimeters (a few inches) to 30 cm (1 ft.) deep, developed as an effect or cause of an ice lens during the rise of a plug. Observations at the Taylor River bend (see the section "Miscellaneous Observations") involving a sequence of forms argue for thawing of ice lenses near the base of a plug as being the principal cause there. Some less conical depressions might be of similar origin or might be related to the plug depressions cited under 3b in this section.

Pattern: Review

1. Plug circles are dominantly circular on near-horizontal surfaces and elongate downslope where the gradient increases; in places elongate circles tend to become linear and somewhat stripelike parallel to the gradient, but no fully developed S-stripes originating in plug circles and plugs were noted in the Resolute area.

2. The size of plug circles can vary more than the size of associated plugs, depending on whether a circle is on a slope and subject to mass-wasting as in 1 in this section, or whether a plug is just starting to emerge at the ground surface or has already reached its full development there as a circle. Differences in soils and moisture may also influence circle and plug size, as shown for instance between plug circles of a rather uniform diameter on a stony slope merging with larger patterns of presumably comparable origin in finer and moister soils at the base of the slope in the area east of the TACAN building (see the section "Transitional Patterned-Ground Forms").

3. Plugs and plug circles associated with emerged beaches tend to parallel them, forming plug and plug-circle rows, but some rows immediately below the inner edge of a bench lie at a slight angle to the inner edge, as upslope of ES C.

4. In places plug rows in gravel overlie plug ridges from which plugs and plug circles arise as pinnacles, as at PE 82-5 (see the section "Occurrences in Emerged Beach Gravel").

5. Plug-circle rows tend to be characterized by plug S-semicircles (see the section "Terminology—patterned ground"), convex upslope, whose upslope sides form a more or less continuous, but in detail discontinuous, shallow depression as at PE 89-2, 90-1 (Figs. 24, 27) (see the section "Occurrences in Emerged Beach Gravel"). These depressions are commonly much less sharply defined than those associated with obvious permafrost cracks above ice wedges in the same area.

6. In places plug S-circles are transitional to other patterns, including RB S-circles, especially in high-moisture environments. Transitions also occur from small circular forms to netlike S-plug patterns within larger forms, with the small units consisting of relatively fresh-appearing soil from depth (see the section "Transitional Patterned-Ground Forms").

7. The size of bordering stones in S-polygons tends to be directly related to polygon diameter (King and Buckley, 1969, p. 116). Also, small S-patterns are commonly associated with more small than large stones and large patterns with more large stones than small (Goldthwait, 1976, p. 33; Thom, 1981, p. 74–75, 141–142; cf. p. 150–151). Such correlations were also cited by Ballantyne and Matthews (1982, p. 345–346). Hallet (1990, p. 845–849) discussed the size relation of stones to pattern in sorted stripes from a modeling perspective.

Pattern: Discussion

1. The tendency for plug rows and associated circles to be aligned more or less parallel to emerged beach lines and a similar alignment of plug ridges and plug semicircles suggest a common control. Several hypotheses, not necessarily mutually exclusive, present themselves.

a. In places the general parallelism may be due to permafrost cracking, which tends to parallel beaches (Fig. 6), with the cracks becoming collecting sites for fines that then become protoplug ridges. The affinity of plugs for permafrost cracks and the presence of a plug resting directly on an ice wedge as at PE 86-4 (see the section "Occurrences in Emerged Beach Gravel") support the permafrost-crack explanation. However, many plug rows show no evidence of being associated with frost or permafrost cracking. Moreover, plug rows are commonly much more closely spaced than similarly oriented permafrost cracks in the same area (Fig. 6). Overall, some instances of plug parallelism are probably due to permafrost cracks, but many others are not.

b. The parallelism may be due to sedimentation whereby washed beach gravel comes to overlie beds containing a significant content of fines, as in marine offlap. Where the beach gravel is thin enough so that the beds with fines extend into the active layer, plugs begin to develop. The sedimentation hypothesis is consistent with several plug excavations, such as PE 82-5 (Fig. 16A–16B) and PE 90-1 (Fig. 29) (see the section "Occurrences in Emerged Beach Gravel"), which show openwork gravel or sand interspersed with irregular layers of fines-rich gravel. However, depth of excavation was usually limited by permafrost, and probable fluctuations of the permafrost table and thickness of the active layer over time, combined with translocation of fines in the active layer, suggest that the irregular diamicton layers may not always be primary.

c. The parallelism may be due to beach-related undulations in the frost table and permafrost table, resulting in subsurface ponding of groundwater (cf. Sollid and Sørbel, 1988, p. 55), accumulation of fines, and presumed intensified frost heaving by ice lenses, some perhaps of intrusive-ice origin, as suggested by J. R. Mackay (personal communication, 1996). The common presence of a thaw basin below fines encircled by gravel (see the section "Other characteristics: Discussion, 5a and b") would create the same effect. Such irregularities in the frost or permafrost table accord with observations at ES C (Fig. 8) and PE 89-2 (Fig. 24).

2. Plug S-circles in disintegrating bedrock (see the section "Occurrences in Disintegrating Bedrock") are inconsistent with soil circulation in plugs, as illustrated by PE 82-4 (Figs. 43, 44) and PE 86-3 (Figs. 45–49). Also, many plug circles and plugs consisting primarily of gravel with mainly interstitial fines argue against a circulatory regime. Examples include PE 90-1 (Sp. 90-8-24) and PE 90-2 (Sp. 90-9-3A) (Table 4) and PE 95-1 (Sp. 95-8-20-1 series), PE 95-2 (Sp. 95-8-20-2 series), and PE 95-3 (Sp. 95-8-21 series) (Figs. 32, 33, 35; Tables 7, 9, 11).

3. Although in places continued plug activity may be apparent only, simulated by strictly surficial frost heaving having generated fresh-appearing soil by inhibiting growth of vegetation, it is commonly real. The continual exposure of fresh fines by surface erosion is probably important, as at PE 89-2 (Fig. 25) (see the section "Occurrences in Emerged Beach Gravel"). Continuity considerations would be met by soil that was formerly just below the permafrost table's becoming incorporated in the active layer, thereby maintaining active-layer equilibrium thickness. Similar considerations were cited by Shilts (1973, p. 9–10, his Fig. 3a; cf. 1978, p. 1065–1066) for mud boils on the slopes below the crest of a drumlin in central Keewatin, northern Canada. He applied the concept quite convincingly in the context of diapirism due to increase in hydrostatic pressure.

Other characteristics: Review

1. Plugs on Cornwallis Island are underlain by permafrost and commonly have ice masses at or near their base and the permafrost table as reported by Mackay (1953, p. 35) and confirmed by excavations during the present investigation, as at PE 82-6, PE 85-8, and PE 90-2 (see the section "Occurrences in Emerged Beach Gravel").

2. Plugs and plug circles in disintegrating bedrock strata closely reflect the strike and lithologic variations of the strata, as at PE 82-4 and PE 86-3 (see the section "Occurrences in Disintegrating Bedrock").

3. Some plug circles lie preferentially along one side or the other of obvious permafrost cracks, as at PE 86-6 (see the section "Occurrences in Emerged Beach Gravel"). Where a crack runs along contours, the circles commonly lie on the downslope side of the crack, but exceptions occur.

4. Many plugs, especially in gravel, have a subsurface upslope-directed neck or, as shown in such excavations as PE 82-5 (see the section "Occurrences in Emerged Beach Gravel"), a low ridge of similar soil connecting a series of plugs

(cf. Egginton, 1972, p. 63–64). Plug necks tended to consist of finer soil than in associated plugs and were at least several tens of centimeters long. Most necks were oriented up and down the slope or at a slight angle to it.

5. Plugs tend to thaw deeper than adjacent openwork gravel, commonly resulting in a shallow bowl-shaped depression in the frost table. This was indicated when probing the central areas of plug circles and adjacent openwork gravel resulted in "soupy" sediment on the tip of a probe and/or its deeper penetration, and a bowl-shaped thaw depression was commonly encountered in plug excavations, as at PE 86-6 at ES C.

Other characteristics: Discussion

1. That plugs generally have ice masses at or near their base and the permafrost table reflects, in part, the fact that ice tends to be especially common near the permafrost table. Mackay (1981, p. 1674) reported that in the Mackenzie Delta region of Canada's Western Arctic, "Winter excavations and drilling at Garry Island have shown that most ice lensing is at the bottom of the active layer and not at the top. . . . " He calculated that upward freezing from the permafrost table might account for about 5 cm of ice lensing during the freeze-back. Total active-layer heave, however, would be reduced by desiccation of the zone between the downward and upward freezing fronts.

2. Summer ice lensing and heaving resulting from downward migration of water to, and into, frozen ground and its refreezing there is also important (Mackay, 1981, p. 1674–1676; 1983). The movement of water into the frozen ground can be aided by the presence of unfrozen films of pore water. In reviewing the evidence for such ice concentrations and frost heaving, Mackay cited the important laboratory work of Ershov (1979), Ershov et al. (1980, p. 172), Pissart (1972), and Zhestkova (1978, 1980); the field studies of Cheng (1982), McGaw et al. (1978), and Parmuzina (Lagov and Parmuzina, 1978; Parmuzina, 1978, 1979, 1980); and Mackay's own detailed and very extensive field observations on Garry Island and elsewhere in the Mackenzie River Delta region. Mackay (1981, p. 1675–1676) observed a thaw-season heave of 14.4 mm consequent on thaw water infiltrating the frozen soil of a hummock at Garry Island. With reference to the implications for the origin of patterned ground, he noted that "Summer ice lensing may help to explain the upward movement of some forms of patterned ground, such as sorted circles of the plug variety (e.g. Cook, 1956; Mackay, 1953), that are not readily explained as freeze-back phenomena" (Mackay, 1983, p. 130).

Further discussions pertinent to the distribution of ice lenses and associated frost heaving include those of S. A. Harris (1986, p. 27–30; 1988) and Pissart (1990, p. 122–123).

3. S-circles and other patterned ground in permafrost areas are associated with special hydrologic conditions. Subsurface water flow tends to be widespread in the active layer because movement of thaw water and rain to depth is retarded, but not necessarily eliminated, by a frost table and the permafrost table. Irregularities in depth to these horizons may result in ponding of groundwater, followed by freezing, then thawing of ice sills and sudden release of ponded water (Woo and Steer, 1983, p. 984–985). Additionally, subsurface flow is probably promoted by increased hydraulic conductivity as ice lenses thaw (L. Dyke and Egginton, 1988, 1990; Egginton and Dyke, 1990). In silty clayey till and in sandy ice-contact and outwash deposits in central Banks Island, N.W.T., subsurface flow exceeds the surface flow to streams (Lewkowicz and French, 1982). Subsurface flow in openwork gravel, although some 2.5 times less than the surface flow on clay to gravel in the Resolute area (Woo and Steer, 1983, p. 985), probably exceeds the surface flow.

4. Possible origins of plug necks include erosion protection, crack fillings, and a role as plug-feeders.

a. Erosion protection was suggested in several places by an overlying stone whose shape conformed to the width of a neck segment, thus partially protecting the neck from subsurface flow and erosion and thereby leaving a relatively high profile during lowering of the frost table. However, the partial nature of such protection argues against its importance.

b. A probable origin for some necks is their development as a frost- or permafrost-crack filling. In one case (PE 86-6; see the section "Occurrences in Emerged Beach Gravel"), a neck was clearly associated with an up- and downslope, ice-wedge crack. Strongly transverse necks were rare or absent, but segments of plug ridges, as at PE 82-5 (see the section "Occurrences in Emerged Beach Gravel"), might seem to be so in a small excavation. An origin as a frost- or permafrost-crack filling would still accommodate a plug-feeder role.

c. A plug-feeder origin is based on the supposition that the site of a neck may have channeled fines under artesian head to the site of plug development, with the channel subsequently becoming blocked with sediment. However, a network of feeders " . . . joining all nearby [plugs] in a system," as reported by Egginton (1972, p. 64), was not observed.

5. a. The shallow, bowl-shaped thaw depression beneath a thawing plug is significant because it promotes accumulation of fines, both as a collecting basin in sufficiently porous and well-drained soil and as a high-moisture environment for weathering or coarser material. Mackay (1979, 1980) assigned a critical role to the depression in his freeze-thaw pumping hypothesis.

b. In addition, the temperature difference between a thaw depression and the surrounding soil can be an important influence on the orientation of freezing and thawing fronts and thereby on stresses and the migration of soil particles.

c. Observations of differential thaw in sorted patterned ground were reported by, among others, Büdel

(1960, p. 47–49, his Fig. 7; p. 54–58, his Fig. 10; 1961, p. 352; 1987, p. 62), Bunting and Jackson (1970, p. 199), Elton (in Huxley and Odell, 1924, p. 226–227),[9] Paterson (1940, p. 116), Schmertmann and Taylor (1965, p. 59–61, 74), Sharp (1942, p. 280–281), and Shilts (1978, p. 1059). Such thaw depressions were also reported by Gripp (1929, p. 158–159) in RB S-circles in Spitsbergen and diagrammed (Gripp, 1952, Abb. 1, p. 116) for pluglike forms that illustrated his concept of the origin of the circles by soil circulation due to moisture-controlled differences in soil density. Bowl-shaped thaw depressions can also occur in nonsorted patterned ground (Hopkins and Sigafoos, 1951, p. 82–83, their Fig. 28; p. 88–89, their Fig. 30; Shilts, 1978, p. 1059), and Mackay (1979, 1980) regarded the presence of such a depression as an essential element in soil circulation in hummocks (discussed later in the section "Hypotheses of Origin, Soil circulation due to freeze-thaw pumping"). However common such a thaw bowl may be in the active layer below circular patterned ground, as reported above, its presence at the permafrost table itself appears to be less commonly noted, perhaps because many field studies terminate before the maximum thaw depth is reached, as suggested by J. R. Mackay (personal communication, 1996). Bunting and Jackson (1970, their Fig. 6, p. 201) and Shilts (1978, p. 1059) cited the occurrence of a thaw bowl at the permafrost table in the Canadian Arctic and Zhu et al. (1993, p. 998), in the Antarctic.

d. Other conditions being constant, soil temperature can be strongly influenced, sometimes in complex fashion, by water content, texture, and presence or absence of insulating vegetation. Water flowing through either vegetated or nonvegetated soil commonly promotes thawing, whereas stagnant water under otherwise similar conditions can be an insulator (Repelewska-Pekalowa and Gluza, 1988, p. 449; their Figs. 4–7, p. 451–452; their Tables II–IV, p. 452–453), with soil texture being a major factor in determining to what extent water is able to move through the soil. Sharp (1942, p. 288–290) noted that moisture changes in fines and gravel can be a critical variable in sorted patterns, influencing rate of thawing and seasonal changes in thaw depth of central areas and borders, including possible reversal in depth. Deeper thaw in the borders than centers was regarded as general by Goldthwait (1976, p. 31). Shilts (1978, p. 1059) explained his observations of deeper thaw in a mud boil than in the border by the saturated mud's having a higher conductivity than the adjacent vegetation, peat, or gravel. The importance of water in furthering the thermal conductivity of peat, normally an excellent insulator, has been discussed by Swanson and Rothwell (1986). On the other hand, frozen icy peat has a high thermal conductivity.

Perhaps the main factors accounting for deeper thaw in plugs than in adjacent soil at Resolute include (1) early exposure of plug circles to thawing because their often convex surfaces favor a relatively thin snow cover, (2) albedo differences whereby thawing of plugs is promoted by their being commonly darker colored than the surrounding carbonate clasts, (3) promotion of infiltration of water to depth by any cracks in plugs (cf. Vasil'yevskaya, 1979, p. 393), and (4) very importantly, the normally increasing thermal conductivity of soil with increasing moisture content (Kersten, 1949, p. 32–61) that would favor thawing of the moisture-retaining plug fines compared with bordering coarse soil that permitted relatively rapid drainage and drying. This effect would be increased to the extent that dead air space builds up in the borders and provides insulation that slows temperature increases and promotes borders' becoming a cold sink (cf. Sharp, 1942, p. 289–290).

During freeze-up at Resolute, Cook (1955, p. 244–247; his Fig. 5 and Table 3) observed a much faster freezing of shattered rock and gravel than of nearby clay and explained it by the zero-curtain effect whereby, compared to the gravel, cooling in the clay is delayed by its greater water content and greater release of latent heat during the freezing process as affected by the freezing-point depression in most fine-grained soils. Freeze-thaw events can contribute significantly to important nonconductive processes involved in the zero-curtain effect (Outcalt et al., 1990).

Cook (1955, p. 239, 243) observed that at a depth of 51 cm (20 in.), about 12.5 cm above the permafrost table, the soil temperatures in clay and in shattered rock and gravel ranged from –0.17 to –.22 °C (31.7 to 31.6 °F) during 1–12 September 1955 (cf. Appendix B, Table 1). By 12 September, the clay had frozen solid to a depth of 12.7 cm (5 in.), the shattered rock and gravel had frozen to a depth of 30.5 cm (12 in.), and there had been 2.5 cm (1 in.) of upward freezing from the permafrost table. However, the clay remained at –0.22 °C for another 5 days while the temperature in the shattered rock and gravel dropped daily. By 19 September the clay was hard frozen to a depth of 25.4 cm (10.0 in.), the upward freezing from the permafrost table had risen a total of 12.5 cm to the 51-cm depth, and the shattered rock and gravel were hard frozen throughout.

It should be noted that upward movement of plugs due to upward freezing from a frost or permafrost table could enable plugs to penetrate overlying dry openwork gravel that was at a negative temperature but nevertheless loose, as described in connection with PE 90-2 at ES C.

The above discussions indicate the complexities that may arise in explaining the difference in the freezing and thawing of plugs and adjacent soil. The fact that thaw depth can exceed 1.0 m in dry gravel and be only 0.4 m in clayey slopes in the Resolute area (Woo and Steer, 1982, p. 2371–2372) is not necessarily contradictory to the preceding explanations for shallower thaw in initially ice-rich gravel, since continually moist, low-angle clayey slopes tend to carry some insulating vegetation, however meager, and other conditions such as ice content and albedo differ within the area (Ming-ko Woo, personal communication, 1988).

Observations in other regions

Pluglike patterned ground is reported from a number of regions, as indicated below, and is perhaps far more widely distributed than is generally recognized. Terminology problems abound, as discussed in the sections "Terminology—patterned ground" and "Terminology—soils."

1. Canadian Arctic
   a. Cornwallis Island (summarized in the section "Earlier Observations" [Cook, 1956; Egginton, 1972; Mackay, 1953; Nichols, 1953]).
   b. Devon Island (Bunting and Jackson, 1970).
   c. Melville Peninsula and Igloolik Island (Dredge, 1992, p. 317, his Fig. 7—S-circles).
   d. Prince of Wales Island (A. S. Dyke et al., 1992, p. 51, their Fig. 37—"Till diapirs").
   e. Victoria Island (Washburn, 1950, p. 39–42; 1956, p. 844). These observations showed that multiple plugs in openwork beach gravel can rest on the nearly horizontal surface of a buried boulder carrying a thin (1 to 2 cm thick) layer of fines (Fig. 69). The boulder, which appeared to be based in permafrost, probably served as a collecting horizon for downward sifting fines. The presence here of significant upward seepage stress was unlikely because of the openwork nature of the gravel. The absence of any silty bed in the adjacent gravel argued against the former presence of a silty stratigraphic horizon that might have served as the source of the fines. This leaves upward freezing, step by step with the accumulation of even a thin layer of fines, as a probable explanation for this occurrence.
2. Greenland (Corte, 1962b, p. 72–76, his Figs. 100a–100b; 1963, p. 20–21, his Fig. 11).
3. Spitsbergen (Bibus, 1976, p. 104–105; his Fig. 6, p. 111; Büdel, 1961, p. 356, his Fig. 5; Büdel, 1987, p. 71, his Fig. 13; Etzelmüller and Sollid, 1991, p. 184, their Fig. 3; p. 189–190, their Fig. 8; Jahn, 1963, p. 140, his Figs. 1–4; p. 144, his Fig. 16).

Figure 69. Plugs exhumed from beach gravel and resting on boulder in permafrost. Hammer as scale. Vicinity Holman, Victoria Island, N.W.T. (Washburn, 1950, Pl. 8, his Fig. 1, p. 40.)

HYPOTHESES OF ORIGIN

General

The origin of plugs and plug circles impacts the origin of several other forms of patterned ground. Consequently the following brief review of hypotheses includes the origin of sorted and nonsorted circles generally, which is still poorly understood (as noted by Dredge, 1992, p. 321), as well as of plug circles specifically.

Much of the older literature tends to be confusing or vague with respect to details of basic processes. Historically and continuing to the present, radial frost sorting and density differences involving load casting (sinking of a soil mass, as opposed to soil particles individually, resulting in compensatory upward displacement of underlying, less dense soil) have attracted much attention, and these hypotheses will be addressed first. Hypotheses based on density differences have usually emphasized soil convection and, more recently, soil circulation, the latter implying a less organized, more complex process than simple fluidlike convection; each is reviewed separately. Also reviewed is the combined significance of (1) the origin of plugs by differential frost heaving, and (2) the importance of upward seepage as a site factor.

The role of frost action in the discussion of hypotheses is not significantly affected by (1) the possibility that temperature changes in bound water in rock in nonfrost climates as well as in frost climates may result in hydration shattering and production of clasts commonly ascribed to frost action in cold climates—a question reviewed by White (1976) and still under investigation; (2) the fact that gilgai in clay-rich swelling soil in some nonfrost climates can form some patterns similar to frost-induced nonsorted nets elsewhere (Washburn, 1979, p. 125, 128, 152, 160); and (3) the fact that nonsorted and sorted desiccation-crack polygons develop in a variety of soils and climates. Except for such occurrences as the above, the widespread combination of shattered rock and patterned ground in alpine and polar regions familiar to me convinces me of the basic importance of frost action in their origin.

Radial frost sorting

General. Stones moving surfaceward relative to finer soil as a result of their upfreezing ("frost jacking") with a descending freezing front and laterally with an inclined freezing front was advanced by Hamberg (1915, p. 605–613). The inclined front could reflect the influence of a bouldery border or soil cracking. Hamberg applied the concept to the origin of debris islands, a variety of S-circle in bouldery mantle, and to other S-circles. Corte (1961, 1962a, 1966) expanded the concept on the basis of laboratory experiments ("horizontal and vertical sorting"). The radial tilting of small wood dowels initially inserted to a depth of 10 cm in the central area of RB S-circles at Resolute (Washburn, 1989) is consistent not only with surficial sorting by "microgelifluction" (Bertouille, 1976) but also with some aspects of convective or circulatory soil movements, as discussed in connection with the next four hypotheses. The question addressed here is to what extent the hypothesis of radial frost sorting as such may apply to the Resolute S-circles, especially the plug forms.

Problems. The following problems argue against radial frost sorting as an overall explanation for the origin of plugs and plug S-circles but not against it as an accessory process in places.

1. Plug S-circles are commonly somewhat domed, with the central areas rising a few centimeters above a uniform stony surface lacking ringlike accumulations of bordering stones from the central area. Rather, bordering stones in the Cornwallis Island beach gravel are commonly distinctly different in being more weathered and angular than those of the plug; moreover, they are of openwork texture throughout their spread, not just adjacent to a plug. Clearly the plug circles significantly postdate the surrounding surface gravel.

2. All gradations from widely spaced, isolated S-circles to closely adjacent circles in an otherwise uniform gravel surface were noted in the then surficially dry outlet of the lake 2 km north of Helen Haven (see the section "Transitional Patterned-Ground Forms"), and it was obvious from their irregular distribution, including isolated circles, that these circles could only have originated from fines-rich soil at depth intruding the overlying gravel, rather than the gravel's having been accumulated by radial sorting. Comparable occurrences elsewhere are widely reported as noted earlier in the section "Characteristics of Plugs and Plug Circles, Morphology, structure, and fabric: Discussion, 1."

3. Similarly, excavation and other observations show that some debris islands, which are probably like plug circles in most respects, are intrusive forms (Schunke, 1975, p. 119, 221; Abh. 11; Washburn, 1969, p. 157, his Fig. 99; p. 158).

Water and soil convection due to density changes in water between 0 and 4 °C

General. Nordenskjöld (1907, p. 565–566), citing Bénard's (1900) experiments with a viscous fluid, suggested that S-polygons are due to convection resulting from thaw water's warming above 0 °C at the surface and, with density increasing to a maximum at 4 °C, sinking along cell borders and carrying fines downward in stony soil in the process, then cooling to 0 °C in contact with the underlying frozen ground, and finally rising and carrying soil upward in the central area to complete the cycle.[10] Repeated cycling supposedly resulted in soil convection. Low (1925) furthered the concept of soil convection by citing the work of Rayleigh (1916) on convective phenomena due to basal heating and by emphasizing the similarity in resulting forms to those in Spitsbergen. The concept of soil convection was vigorously promoted by Gripp (1926; 1927, p. 10–16; 1929, p. 154–161) on the basis of his Spitsbergen observations.

Problems. The hypothesis in its original form was soon discarded in view of evidence that the density difference in water was too small to drive soil convection (Elton, 1927; Mortensen, 1932, 1934; and others) or was inconsistent with observed temperature profiles (Poser, 1931, p. 221–222; Jahn, 1946, p. 87; Jahn, 1948, p. 56–57; and others). Gripp and Simon (1933, 1934a) discounted the early objections, but subsequently Gripp (1952, p. 113–117) changed his views, as reviewed later.

Modified hypothesis—A free-convection model. The importance of density changes in water has been recently revived in a modified hypothesis whereby soil convection may not be essential to circle genesis; only the pore-water convection is needed because it may thermally imprint a pattern on the permafrost table that then guides the development of soil cells by other processes (Gleason et al., 1988; Krantz et al., 1988; Ray et al., 1983). This hypothesis, which presents a comprehensive, free-convection model of self organization with potential applicability to S-patterned ground, has been reviewed in updated form by Krantz (1990). Although the free-convection model of Krantz and his coauthors lacks detailed field corroboration, a quantitative approach permitting verifiable predictions is much to be desired and would offer the possibility of new insights. Various problems would need to be addressed.

Problems.

1. The objections of Poser (1931, p. 221–222), Jahn (1946, p. 87; 1948, p. 56–57), and others to soil convection based on density changes in water may still be applicable, in part, to the water-convection process.

2. Hallet (1993, p. 152) suggested that

> the excellent accord between the predicted aspect ratio of water convection cells and field measurement of the size of sorted polygons in diverse settings . . . may be misleadingly appealing; convection of water may have little to do with the initiation of patterned ground. Our field studies of active sorted circles in western Spitsbergen indicate

that water is not convecting but that the soil undergoes long term circulatory motion comprised of yearly increments punctuated by seasonal freezing and thawing. Evidence for this frost-induced soil circulation together with the observation that sorted circles generally occur only in areas rich in fine-grained sediments, which essentially preclude free convection of water due to their low permeability and the weak driving force, suggest that the aspect ratio of sorted patterns is dictated by soil circulation. The accord between the sorted pattern geometry and the water convection model may then be simply incidental, and non-diagnostic because the aspect ratio of convection cells in homogeneous material is rather universal for a diversity of systems and driving mechanisms.

3. The models have not been amplified and field checked with respect to (1) detailed temperature profiles throughout the thaw season, (2) observations of pore-water convection in patterned ground, and (3) the actual pattern imprinted on the permafrost table as related to (1) and (2).

4. Isolated plug circles of various sizes in otherwise uniform terrain conditions do not appear to fall within the conceptual framework.

Soil circulation due to freeze-thaw pumping[11]

General. It has been proposed that hummocks (Mackay, 1979, 1980) or N-circles (Veillette, 1980, p. 259–267) can be explained by a pumplike volume expansion and contraction of the soil as the result of (1) freezing and soil expansion in the upper and lower parts of the active layer, (2) concurrent desiccation and contraction of the central part as water moves outward from it toward both the downward-moving freezing front from the surface and an upward-moving freezing front from the permafrost table, and (3) thawing and collapse of the soil except in the desiccated central part, which expands as it absorbs thaw water (Fig. 70). The thawing and collapse of the soil is guided by a bowl-shaped thaw depression in the active layer, as discussed by Mackay. Thaw depressions in hummocks have also been described by Crampton (1977), but their role is differently interpreted. Such depressions have been long known in N-circles and S-circles (see the section "Characteristics of Plugs and Plug Circles, Other characteristics: Review, 5; Discussion, 5a").

In Mackay's hypothesis, the pumplike action causes upward intrusion of mud and a "cell circulation" (Mackay, 1980, p. 1005). "The thawed bottom muds typically have a water content beyond the liquid limit, void ratios are high, effective stresses are low, and shear strengths are, therefore, negligible (Fig. 5). Tongues of soft mud can often be observed in hummock excavations to originate at and to rise upwards from the frost table (Fig. 6)" (Mackay, 1980, p. 1000). The tongues are "squeezed" upward (cf. Mackay, 1979, p. 165–166). "In late summer, the buoyancy effect which follows a rain would, it is suggested, exert an auxiliary pumping action on saturated bottom mud" (Mackay, 1980, p. 1002). In Mackay's model, the bottom soil would be replaced by soil from the surface moving outward, downward, and then inward and upward under the gravitational influence of the domed surface and the bowl-shaped basal thaw depression, with the upward movement resulting from the pumplike action, the end result according to the hypothesis being soil circulation (Fig. 70).

Although Mackay (1979) suggested that his hypothesis might be applicable to some other types of patterned ground, he specifically noted that the hummocks to which he applied it should not be confused with mud boils described from Keewatin, which compared to hummocks are much lower in clay content, liquid limit, and plasticity index (Mackay, 1980, p. 998–999). Veillette (1980, p. 267), however, favored the hypothesis for such mud boils, and application of Mackay's concept to plugs and plug circles merits serious consideration.

As noted earlier in the section "Radial frost sorting," the surficial soil in the central areas of RB S-circles at Resolute moved radially toward the borders at ES B. Thermistor cable observations in these circles were not sufficiently detailed to prove the existence of a bowl-shaped thaw depression but appeared to be consistent with it. Also, as previously discussed in the section "Transitional Patterned-Ground Forms," some plug S-circles in disintegrating bedrock near ES B appeared to be transitional to normal S-nets that were, in turn, apparently transitional to the RB S-circles at ES B. The dome-shaped surface and the bowl-shaped thaw depression that are so important to the freeze-thaw pumping hypothesis were definitely present in Resolute plug S-circles (see the section "Characteristics of Plugs and Plug Circles," as cited above). Nevertheless, application of the freeze-thaw pumping hypothesis to the plugs and plug S-circles as an overall explanation encounters difficulties.

Problems. The problems apply primarily to soil circulation in plugs and plug circles but not to the upward movement of mobile fine soil to which Mackay drew attention and which could be interpreted as due to upward seepage and frost heaving without the soil becoming subject to circulation, as discussed later in the section "Differential frost heaving and surfaceward seepage." Because circulation is reviewed next, in "Soil circulation due to moisture-controlled changes in density," further discussion is deferred to that section.

Soil circulation due to moisture-controlled changes in density

General. Mortensen (1932, p. 421–422) recognized that temperature-controlled water convection in soil was too weak to cause soil convection, a point still requiring emphasis by Bertouille (1978, p. 29) almost half a century later. However, Mortensen also indicated that soil instability arising from relatively dense stony soil overlying less dense wet soil in a profile that was already sorted in this manner was likely to be unstable and might lead to soil convection. He suggested that debris islands (a variety of S-circle) might be explained in this way. Such an instability can be promoted by soil density changes due to elevated pore pressures sustained by thawing ice lenses. The importance of such density changes was also recognized by

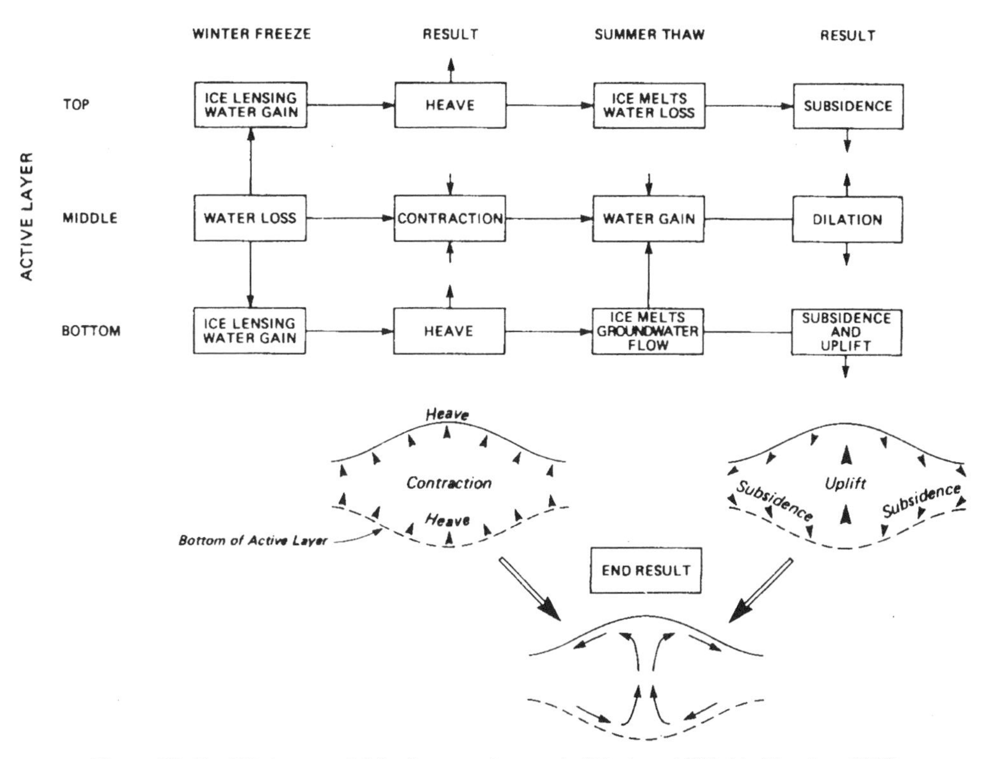

Figure 70. Equilibrium model for hummock growth (Mackay, 1980, his Fig. 4, p. 1000).

Gripp and Simon (1933, p. 434–435; 1934b, p. 286) and especially by Sørensen (1935, p. 32–53), who presented a carefully reasoned and frequently overlooked analysis based on his observations in northeast Greenland. Among other things he included movement of stones by upfreezing, thereby meeting Mohaupt's (1932, p. 49) criticism of Gripp's early views on soil convection. Gripp (1952, p. 113–117) eventually accepted soil convection due to moisture-controlled changes in soil density instead of temperature-controlled convection of water itself as the critical process responsible for RB S-circles. There is a large patterned-ground literature on the subject, and a review of the early literature is given elsewhere (Washburn, 1956, p. 854–855).

Basic soil-mechanics principles apply to considerations of moisture-controlled changes in soil density of the active layer. As thaw water from ice in the soil or from snow saturates the soil, excess pore water moves upward during soil consolidation, thereby reducing effective (intergranular) stress and favoring development of an unstable density gradient. A heavy rain could contribute to the effect. The effective stress in a vertical column of soil is defined as

$$\sigma_e = \sigma_t - u_o \tag{1}$$

where σ_e = effective stress, σ_t = total stress, and u_o = pore-water pressure, which is hydrostatic (neutral). Similarly, presence of an upward seepage stress from rising pore water is defined as

$$\sigma_e = \sigma_t - u_o - u_s \tag{2}$$

where seepage stress, u_s, is the force per unit area transferred from the water percolating through a porous granular medium to the medium itself by means of viscous friction. This stress decreases the effective stress at the same depth, thereby facilitating soil deformation and specifically a tendency for soil to move upward. Depending on the magnitude of the stresses involved, this rise could entrain fine soil particles only or coarser as well.

Various situations arise resulting in upward seepage sufficiently forceful to entrain soil, but all are variations of the same basic definition expressed in eq. 2. A common situation is that of subsurface flow (see the section "Characteristics of Plugs and Plug Circles, Other characteristics: Discussion, 3") under a hydraulic gradient encountering an abrupt decrease in slope or in soil permeability, thereby diverting subsurface flow laterally and/or upward. Upward seepage with entrained soil particles would be especially favored where relatively low-density soil underlies denser soil, thereby giving rise to a reverse density gradient. Such reversal, for instance, might result from (1) original sedimentation, (2) upfreezing of stones from underlying fines in an initially normal density gradient, or (3) drying of higher-lying relatively impermeable soil whereby continuity of water with underlying soil containing excess water is lost and the entire weight of the overlying soil, including any pore water, becomes an effective stress promoting instability of lower-lying soil (cf. Egginton and Dyke, 1982).[12]

Soil circulation resulting from thawing of alpine S-circles in Norway was inferred by C. Harris and Cook (1988), and by

C. Harris (1990) in Colorado. In the former study the detailed examination of two S-circles revealed upward displacement of soil whose microfabrics were interpreted as indicating upward injection of "liquidized sediment within circle centres during thaw" (C. Harris and Cook, 1988, p. 780). Soil circulation consequent on density displacement of soil during thawing or resulting from differential frost heaving was inferred as the origin of soil nets on Mount Albion in the Colorado Front Range by Benedict (1978, p. 19–41). His observation of lateral displacement of artifacts at the surface and their presence at depth in the central area suggested soil circulation. Subsequently, on the basis of extensive observations on Niwot Ridge in the Front Range, he stressed density displacement due to disturbance of metastable systems. "Plugs of mobile low-density fine material rise upward into the high-density rubble layer" (Benedict, 1992, p. 16). The cause of the collapse of the metastable layer "was by no means clear."

Evidence for circulation of stones (as opposed to soil mass as a whole) in small (20- to 30-cm-diameter) S-polygons in Öland, Sweden, was advanced by Rydquist (1960, p. 68–71, 74). He found in an approximately 20-cm-thick soil layer over bedrock a consistent decrease in percent of lichen-covered stones from the top of the stony border (100%) to its base (60%), then laterally to the base of the central region (50%) and above it (20%) to 3 to 4 cm below the surface (10%). This trend suggesting progressive alteration was accompanied by decreasing stone size. Orientation of plant roots was cited as showing a lateral movement of stones at depth from border toward center. A similar inward and upward movement of soil inferred from the attitude of plant roots was reported from Swedish Lapland by Wassén (1965, p. 236; 1966, p. 92; his Fig. 60(e), p. 93).

Also highly pertinent are the important field observations in northern Canada and the resulting conclusions by Mackay (1979, 1980) and Veillette (1980), discussed in the preceding section, "Soil circulation due to freeze-thaw pumping," and the field evidence cited by A. S. Dyke and Zoltai (1980) for circulation in mud boils in Keewatin, Boothia Peninsula, and Somerset Island. Here radiocarbon-dated soil revealed a downward and lateral inward movement at depth; the upward central movement was inferred on general principles. Deduced average movement rates ranged from some 0.5 mm to 1.0 mm/yr, implying that the mud boils had occupied the same sites for several thousand years. These observations on mud boils and Shilts's (1978, p. 1054) reference to Mackay's (1953) and Cook's (1956) mud circles (plug circles of the present report) as "mudboil-like features" suggest the possibility that soil liquefaction and soil rise due to moisture-controlled changes in soil density involving significant upward seepage stress, might also be responsible for some other circular forms of patterned ground, including plug circles.

Problems.

1. The mosaic nature of clasts where domed by underlying plugs and of bordering clasts in emerging plug S-circles in disintegrating bedrock (see the section "Characteristics of Plugs and Plug Circles, Pattern: Discussion, 2") is definitive evidence against soil circulation as a genetic process in these forms. Any circulation here would be essentially limited to illuviation of some fines to depth along fractures in the disintegrating bedrock, heaving of these fines and any associated fragments from underlying disintegrating bedrock, and quite possibly subsequent reilluviation of some fine particles but probably rarely fragments larger than granules (2 to 4 mm diameter). Border stability is also shown by RB plug S-circles that are not obviously in disintegrating bedrock. Although the central areas of most such Resolute circles are active, as shown by the fresh, unweathered character of fines, clasts, and commonly of any shells, the borders are relatively very stable, as indicated by such weathering effects as marked color changes in border fines and clasts, etching of clasts, and the in-situ fracturing of such clasts.

2. Cross sections of plugs and RB S-circles at Thule, northwest Greenland, show little if any evidence of sorting or structures indicative of soil circulation (Corte, 1962b, his Figs. 100a–100b, cf. p. 72–73; 1963, p. 20–21, his Fig. 11). Also, grain-size analyses of S-circles in the same area led Schmertmann and Taylor (1965, p. 71, 74) to conclude that evidence of radial sorting was confined to approximately the upper 60 cm (2 ft.) of the active layer, which was some 90 to 120 cm (3 to 4 ft.) thick (Schmertmann and Taylor, 1965, their Figs. 39, p. 52; 44, p. 60; 51, p. 69).

3. The soil-circulation concept is largely based on laboratory experiments that rarely meet field conditions, including the slow thaw consolidation (rapid thawing) required to retain excess pore water and the necessary density difference upon thawing (Van Vliet-Lanoë, 1988a, p. 472–477; 1988b, p. 87; 1989b).

Note: This criticism is weakened to the extent that soil circulation may occur without soil liquefaction, as argued by Hallet and Waddington (1991, p. 253), as cited below in the note following problem 4. Also, Hallet's strong support of soil circulation is primarily based not on laboratory studies but on detailed field study of RB S-circles in Spitsbergen.

4. In places cryogenic microfabrics and micromorphology suggest a stability generally incompatible with liquefaction in the context of soil circulation (Van Vliet-Lanoë, 1988a, p. 537; 1988b, p. 89; 1988c, p. 1010–1011; 1989b). In elaborating her recent views, Van Vliet-Lanoë (1991, p. 134) mentioned convection and "circulatory patterns" and cited observations presented by Mackay (1980, 1983), Hallet and Prestrud (1986), and Hallet et al. (1988) that agree with some of her concepts if interpreted in the context of "differential frost heave and differential swelling," as reviewed later in the section "Differential frost heaving and surfaceward seepage."

Note: This problem is difficult to evaluate, since microfabrics and micromorphology have also been cited in support of soil circulation (C. Harris and Cook, 1988; C. Harris, 1990). The question hinges in part on (1) whether these features are clearly indicative of soil displacement in the thawed condition and preserved during subsequent freezing, (2) whether they might reflect movement during frost heaving with subsequent modification during thawing, or (3) whether a liquefied state is really required at all for soil circulation, provided buoyancy, even small, acts long enough (Hallet and Waddington, 1991, p. 253, 276–277).

Moreover, the problem also involves the probability of considerable deformation of already frozen soils because of volume changes consequent on fluctuations in freezing temperature as reported by Pissart (1976, p. 278–279) and Russian investigators. Presumably this soil behavior reflects the freezing and thawing of unfrozen water at subfreezing temperatures, as reviewed elsewhere (Washburn, 1979, p. 100–102), and perhaps deformation from additional moisture movement to already frozen soil, as suggested by Smith and Patterson (1989). Furthermore, deformation might occur during frost heaving while the soil is freezing but still somewhat plastic, as might be the case if cryostatic (freezing-induced hydrostatic) pressure were present (Washburn, 1956, p. 842–845), or if lateral stress were generated at depth by inclined freezing fronts resulting from more rapid cooling of large stones or stony border accumulations than of adjacent accumulations of finer soil (cf. Crampton, 1977; Washburn, 1956, p. 842–845). Even though cryostatic pressure in patterned ground may be uncommon because of a desiccated zone in the active layer of frost-susceptible soils (Mackay, 1980, p. 997–998; Mackay and MacKay, 1975), it may be common in nonfrost-susceptible soils that permit expulsion of pore water (Mackay, 1979, p. 165). More recently Van Vliet-Lanoë (1991, p. 134–135) limited the importance of cryostatic pressure to " . . . water logged or poorly drained soils, i.e. on essentially horizontal microtopography."[13]

5. The above problems relating to soil circulation in plugs do not address the question of circulation of plug fines in openwork gravel, as in beaches where fines at plug surfaces may become detached and eluviated to depth to become reincorporated in the same plug. However, this would not constitute circulation of the plug soil as a whole in stony plugs. Experiments involving "tagging" fines and stones might help to provide critical evidence.

6. If the increasing evidence for soil circulation in some RB S-circles is accepted as proof, circulation may be consequent on prior establishment of suitable conditions in transitional forms of well-developed plug circles (Washburn, 1989, p. 953–954).

Soil circulation associated with differential frost heaving

General. Soil circulation associated with differential frost heaving is a relatively new concept. Hallet (1987, 1990) and his coworkers (Hallet and Prestrud, 1986; Hallet et al., 1988; Hallet and Waddington, 1991) have been carrying out detailed studies of the classical RB S-circles of Spitsbergen. They considered in some detail several modes of origin involving soil circulation. These studies led to the conclusion that although the driving force is undetermined, forces associated with differential frost heaving may be very important (Hallet and Waddington, 1991, p. 253, 270). Because of the possibility that plugs and plug circles may be related to RB S-circles, circulation associated with differential frost heaving requires consideration.

Hallet and Waddington in considering soil properties from RB S-circle sites found that the effective Rayleigh number, Ra = 3×10^{-3}, is well below the critical value, and they concluded " . . . that buoyancy-driven circulation of active layer soil is not sustainable . . . " (Hallet and Waddington, 1991, p. 270). They did

> not view buoyancy as being essential or even dominant in the development of many types of patterned ground. Other forces, especially those associated with differential frost heaving, are clearly important in their development due to the large gradients in heaving stresses in soil resulting from local variations in soil texture or moisture (Pissart, 1982; Van Vliet-Lanoë, 1988[c]; Washburn, 1991). In essence, differential frost heaving results from preferential soil heaving in domains where moisture and textural conditions are particularly favorable for segregation ice growth. A critical element of this mechanism is that frost heave tends not to be fully reversible upon thawing. As a consequence, cyclic heave-thaw generally leads to permanent upward motion of soil where recurrent frost heave is most active. The factors responsible for this irreversibility remain somewhat of a mystery.[14] We propose that buoyancy can provide a significant and persistent upward force on frost-susceptible soil at depth through most of the thaw season, exactly what is needed to translate cyclic motion induced by freeze/thaw into long-term net soil motion (Hallet and Waddington, 1991, p. 253).

Their views are further clarified by their summary statement:

> Moreover, the role of buoyancy in long-term soil circulation in active sorted soil patterns should not be discounted. Notably, circulation may arise incrementally from the yearly regeneration of buoyant soil above the thaw front, which tends to induce a seasonal ascent of basal material and a corresponding descent of overlying material even in the absence of stratification. Provided such displacements are spatially organized on the scale of the active layer depth by preexisting lateral variations in texture, as would be expected in well-developed sorted circles, buoyancy could account for the observed pattern and rates of long-term soil circulation (Hallet and Waddington, 1991, p. 276–277).

Although discarding buoyancy as a driving mechanism for soil convection sensu strictu, Hallet and Waddington do not discard it for soil circulation, as has been inferred (Burn and Smith, 1993, p. 163).

Observations of near-surface movement in RB S-circles at Resolute are consistent with soil circulation (Washburn, 1989).

Problems. Although considerable evidence can be advanced supporting soil circulation in RB S-circles in general, further data are needed, similar to the observations from Colorado, northern Canada, and Swedish Lapland cited in the preceding section "Soil circulation due to moisture-controlled changes in density." Pending further evidence, applicability of the soil-circulation concept to the EB plug circles would be problematic. The same problems arise here as were cited in the preceding section.

Soil loading (loadcasting)

General. A reverse density gradient (i.e., density decreasing with depth) may be original with deposition of sediments or may be due to subsequent loading with high-density sediments, resulting in the upward displacement of less dense sediments known as loadcasting[15] in the periglacial literature (cf. Dżułyński, 1963, p. 147; Van Vliet-Lanoë, 1991, p. 134). Loadcasting can also occur with changing conditions such as desiccation of continuous pore water in higher-lying soil and upfreezing of stones. Stability could be achieved when all the underlying light soil reached the surface. Until then, continuity requirements could be met by availability of a continuing supply of uncirculated fines from sources discussed earlier (see the section "Characteristics of Plugs and Plug Circles, Constitution: Discussion, 1–6"). Such a continuing supply would minimize my earlier (Washburn, 1969, p. 121–122) criticism of differential frost heaving as an essential process in the origin of circles.

Soil displacement due to loading is supported by the laboratory experiments and work of Dżułyński and coauthors (Dżułyński, 1963, 1966; Butrym et al., 1964; Anketell et al., 1970; and Cegła, 1973). Most of this work was undertaken in the context of sedimentary features without regard to frost action. However, as Dżułyński (1966, p. 19) noted, "Unstable stratification exists in polar regions, and is due to the segregation caused by frost-heave or deposition of heavier clasts upon the frozen silts." Instability in stratification was also emphasized by Van Vliet-Lanoë (1985, p. 144–146) in introducing and classifying frost-susceptibility gradients as positive or negative, with the negative gradient corresponding to Dżułyński's unstable stratification. However, she interpreted the consequences differently, as promoting frost heaving of mud boils rather than "convection-like movement." (See discussion of Van Vliet-Lanoë's views in the section "Differential frost heaving and surfaceward seepage.") Although Dżułyński and coauthors suggested an analogy with convectionlike movements, their illustrations of experimental features emphasize density displacement, leading to layer inversion, rather than necessarily to the cellular-type movement associated with soil circulation.

Some of the problems cited earlier in connection with changes in soil density driving soil circulation do not apply to density displacement only, independent of soil circulation. Both Jahn (1948, p. 57–59) and Washburn (1956, p. 855; 1969, p. 120–123) stressed diapirism rather than soil circulation, as is also true of most discussions of mud boils in Arctic Canada (Egginton and Shilts, 1978; Egginton, 1979; Egginton, 1981, p. 300; Egginton and Dyke, 1982; and Shilts, 1978, p. 1065–1066; among others).

Problems.

1. As defined above, loadcasting emphasizes loading from above as the critical initiating process, whereas the perspective is depth focused with respect to both frost heaving and upward seepage, as discussed in the next section.

2. Because of liquidity requirements, "Loadcasting can only be effective in waterlogged sites, but even here its existence remains to be demonstrated" (Van Vliet-Lanoë, 1991, p. 134).

3. Except in areas of gilgai, the lack of plugs and other circular patterned ground in nonfrost environments argues against density gradients alone being an explanation for plug circles.

None of the foregoing hypotheses appears to be satisfactory for plugs and plug circles generally. The next section considers a preferred hypothesis.

Differential frost heaving and surfaceward seepage

Differential frost heaving. In one form or another differential frost heaving, sometimes in combination with other processes, is one of the oldest explanations for many circles (including some mud boils) and also for several other patterned-ground forms not dependent on contraction cracking. One of the early proponents was Frödin (1918, p. 21–27); others include Mortensen (1932, p. 421–422), Poser (1933, p. 113–114), Sharp (1942), Taber (1943, p. 1458–1459), Mackay (1953, p. 35), Schenk (1955, p. 53–87), Corte (1962b, p. 72–73), Jahn (1963), Fahey (1975), Nicholson (1976), Pissart (1966, 1976, 1982), and, more recently, Etzelmüller and Sollid (1991, p. 189), Hallet and Waddington (1991, p. 253), Sollid and Sørbel (1988, p. 59–60), Van Vliet-Lanoë (1983; 1988a, p. 479–489, 534–539; 1988b; 1988c; 1991, p. 131, 135–136), Van Vliet-Lanoë and Coutard (1986), and Kling (1996).

I concur in the essential role of differential frost heaving depending on the specific formulation of the hypothesis. Mackay (1953, p. 35) clearly inferred that differential frost heaving was important in the origin of plugs and plug circles, although without claiming that the origin of plugs was thereby satisfactorily explained: "Some of the plugs rest on ice-lenses which may be three or more feet in diameter and a foot or more thick. The lenses are composed predominantly of ice with a few stones and some wafer-like fragments of clay. The growth of the lenses may bow up the overlying material and help to raise the mud plugs." Pissart (1966, 1976) and Nicholson (1976) relied on inclined freezing fronts to explain differential frost heaving in patterned ground (cf. Brown and Gangloff, 1980, their Fig. 7, p. 149) and regarded soil circulation as a consequence.

Van Vliet-Lanoë's (1985, p. 144–146) emphasis on differential frost heaving in the origin of patterned ground is in line with Corte's (1962b, p. 72–73) conclusions regarding its importance in the origin of S-circles, based on his large-scale excavations in Greenland and on laboratory investigations. In elaborating the role of frost heaving, Van Vliet-Lanoë (1985, p. 144–146) introduced the concept of a frost-susceptibility gradient. As described by Van Vliet-Lanoë (1988b, p. 92),

> Field observations in Svalbard show that differential frost heave, resulting from ice lensing, is the main factor of soil deformation both in well drained and in poorly drained situations. These observations enable one

to propose a new theory complementary to that of differential heave. . . . If surface material is more frost-susceptible than underlying sediment (via differences in clay, silt or organic content) the gradient will be positive; here injections [upward intrusions, diapirs] are not able to reach the surface because of the rigid surface layer caused by frost. In the negative gradient situation [underlying sediment more frost susceptible], the injected sediment is able to burst through the surface to form mud boils as observed by Pissart (1976) on Banks Island (N.W.T. Canada). This hypothesis, especially in the presence of a positive gradient, can be extended to explain contiguous stone circles [S-circles], as in Kvadehuk, as the result of expulsion of frost-shattered bedrock along cracking patterns.[16] A marked contrast in frost susceptibility acts as an accelerator; the presence of a thermal contraction crack network is not necessary to explain mudboil formation.

However, Vandenberghe (1992, p. 346) noted that " . . . frost susceptibility does not influence the deformation mechanism, as claimed by Van Vliet-Lanoë (1985)." Vandenberghe's argument was that the same structures may be produced regardless of whether the frost-susceptibility gradient is positive or negative. Although Van Vliet-Lanoë (1991, p. 136) combined the effects of differential frost heaving and differential swelling (her Fig. 5, p. 128; p. 134–136), she regarded the intensity of the latter in periglacial environments as the much less important of the two except in poorly humified organic soils. Van Vliet-Lanoë (1991, p. 134–135) supported the importance of cryostatic pressure but limited its role to waterlogged or poorly drained soils (see the section "Hypotheses of Origin, Soil circulation due to moisture-controlled changes in density, Problems, 4, Note"). Thus in a broad approach, Van Vliet-Lanoë called on differential frost heaving in association with (1) frost-susceptibility gradients and (2) preexisting polygonal cracking that may initiate sites of weakness and permit upward injections that become N-circles or S-circles and also in a more limited way with (3) differential swelling and (4) cryostatic pressure.

Differential frost heaving was cited by Sollid and Sørbel (1988) in describing the spectacular RB S-circles with stony borders up to 50 cm high in the Kvadehuksletta and Ny-Ålesund areas of Spitsbergen. They are " . . . mostly located in the depressions between beach ridges. This location is probably due to the higher water content, and consequently a more effective frost activity" (Sollid and Sørbel, 1988, p. 55); they emphasized differential frost heaving of " . . . plugs or diapir-like structures of fine material . . . " in the origin of RB S-circles but ". . . the exact mechanisms for this process is a matter of discussion . . . " (Sollid and Sørbel, 1988, p. 60). Etzelmüller and Sollid (1991) in their report on the role of weathering in the origin of the RB S-circles at Kvadehuksletta concluded from detailed mineralogical analyses that silt from the dissolution of the dolomitic bedrock of the area accumulated in situ in depressions and by translocation to them. The frost susceptibility of the silt " . . . leads to vertical and lateral mass displacement or differential frost heaving. A dome of fines is formed, which migrates upwards, eventually reaching the surface, producing patterned ground (Sollid and Sørbel, 1988)" (Etzelmüller and Sollid, 1991, p. 189). These interpretations applied to the origin of RB S-circles in Spitsbergen are similar in many respects to the role of differential frost heaving as cited for the plugs and plug circles of the Resolute area (Washburn, 1989, p. 953; 1991).

Surfaceward seepage. Briefly paraphrased, seepage here involves the slow movement of water through sufficiently porous soil, with seepage stress being the force transferred from the water to the soil by viscous friction (cf. AGI/G, p. 599).

As noted in the section "Soil loading (loadcasting)," surfaceward seepage is also the critical process in that context. However, the perspective in the present context differs in that the originating conditions are depth oriented.

Two types of seepage are particularly important in the present context. One is upward expulsion of water during thaw consolidation of ice-rich soil; a second is subsurface water moving downslope on a frost or permafrost table and encountering an effective decrease in slope or in soil permeability or some other constriction in flow. In such situations water rising toward the surface would tend to do so differentially depending on the permeability of the overlying soil and, in a somewhat fluctuating manner, depending on thaw temperatures, precipitation, and seasonal artesian conditions due to freezing of overlying soil. It should be stressed that "surfaceward" does not necessarily imply a vertical component of movement—only that the subsurface water movement on the frost or permafrost table reaches higher in the slope profile. This presumably explains the profusion of plug circles in such places as above ES C and "Summit Lake" (cf. the section "Miscellaneous Observations, Terrain influences").

Surfaceward seepage (1) would promote soil saturation and differential frost heaving during subsequent soil freezing; (2) could supplement buoyancy forces; and (3) under sufficient seepage stress, could entrain fines and, by their deposition higher in the profile, promote the frost susceptibility of overlying soil. With high enough seepage stress, soil liquefaction and relatively rapid surfaceward soil displacement could ensue. Some instances of plug-circle concentrations occurring below marked increases in slope are cited in the section "Miscellaneous Observations, Terrain influences."

Clearly, surfaceward seepage can promote the location of plugs and plug circles. Whether or not it is essential to their origin more generally is not established, but seepage tends to be such a common process where plugs occur to merit its consideration as a very important companion process to differential frost heaving.

The hypothesis that plugs and plug circles owe their development to differential frost heaving and, in places, surfaceward seepage as a very important companion process was outlined by Washburn (1991). The hypothesis requires discussion of the initiation and dynamics of plugs and plug circles.

Initiation. As noted in the earlier section "Characteristics of Plugs and Plug Circles, Constitution: Discussion, 1–6," the fines for plug initiation can be derived from many sources. Because the fines attract and retain moisture they promote more weathering, production of more fines, and hence more ice lensing and heaving. This feedback becomes self-reinforcing once started unless conditions change. It can start in various ways, among the most important being probably (1) preexisting concentrations of fines of whatever origin that retain moisture preferentially and (2) the development of closed depressions or undulations in bedrock or in the frost or permafrost table that favor trapping fines and moisture—for instance, permafrost cracks that focus the development of some plug S-circles, as noted in connection with PE 86-6 and elsewhere at ES C (see the section "Characteristics of Plugs and Plug Circles, Other characteristics: Review, 3"). A comparable situation involving the development of N-circles was noted in Greenland (Washburn, 1969, p. 108, 111).

Concentrations of fines and moisture are likely to have high points that become prime sites for differential frost heaving. That plug soil tends to arise from the permafrost table rather than from higher in the active layer is entirely consistent with the permafrost table's being a primary locus for accumulation of fines and moisture and for growth of ice lenses that would favor initiation of plugs.

Finally, various considerations, such as especially favorable soil conditions, including temperature and moisture gradients, might well trigger and promote plug development. Once a protoplug forms, it would tend to continue developing and moving toward the surface, as discussed below.

Dynamics. Assuming that plugs result from differential frost heaving, with surfaceward seepage being a critical companion process, a continuing supply of frost-susceptible soils to keep pace with any surface erosion is a necessary condition for continuity of heaving. The fines in a frost-susceptible soil can have a number of sources (as indicated in the preceding section) and, depending on the source, can be added to an existing concentration of fines, whether at its base, top, or some intermediate position. The ejection of stones from fines by frost sorting, long recognized by many investigators and detailed by Corte (1961, 1962a, 1966), Bertouille (1976), and Anderson (1988), among others, can also contribute over time to an increased subsurface concentration of fines. Any such increase, especially in silt, would promote ice lensing and increased frost heaving.

Both a frost table and the permafrost table tend to be high-moisture environments favoring ice lensing and heaving when freezing sets in, whether from a freezing front moving downward from the ground surface or moving upward from a frost or permafrost table. Cook's (1955, p. 244–247) observations showed that at Resolute upward freezing could amount to 12.5 cm, extending from a permafrost-table depth of about 63.5 cm (25 in.) to within 51 cm (20 in.) of the surface (cf. the section "Characteristics of Plugs and Plug Circles, Other characteristics: Discussion, 5d").

Frost heaving at depth can also be triggered during the thaw season by water infiltrating below a frost table or permafrost table and refreezing there to cause summer frost heaving, as reviewed earlier, including Mackay's (1983, p. 130) suggestion that such heaving might help to explain plugs (see the section "Characteristics of Plugs and Plug Circles, Other characteristics: Discussion, 2"). Thaw water refreezing in frozen ground and causing heaving was subsequently also stressed by Van Vliet-Lanoë (1988b, p. 86; 1989a; 1989b; 1991, p. 124).

Upward freezing from a frost table rather than from the permafrost table can occur without necessarily involving surface freezing when reversal of heat flow from warming to cooling of the ground surface occurs during cold spells in the thaw season. Tarnocai (1980, p. 325–326) reported an upward fluctuation of the frost table that occurred weeks before surface freezing and amounted to as much as a surprising 30 cm from a depth of 50 cm to 20 cm, based on temperature observations; the maximum depth of thaw lay somewhat deeper than 50 cm but probably near it. Such events lend support to the significance of summer frost heave while surface temperatures remain above freezing, as discussed by Mackay (1983). Consequently both summer frost heaving and upfreezing from the permafrost table can lead to frost heaving of fines-rich soil, which could act as a piston in tending to push up and/or shoulder aside overlying soil, depending on the latter's resistance to deformation.

The Resolute observations show that there is a tendency for fines in plugs to thaw more rapidly than surrounding openwork gravel and therefore to create, and also confirm for plugs, the shallow, bowl-shaped thaw depression (see the section "Characteristics of Plugs and Plug Circles, Other characteristics: Discussion, 5a") that has such an important place in Mackay's (1979, 1980) freeze-thaw pumping hypothesis.

Radially inward-directed freezing from stony borders to finer central areas of patterned ground is probably common because of diffusivity differences, other things being equal (cf. Bertouille, 1976; King and Buckley, 1969, p. 116), and it accords with generally more rapid freezing of coarse than of fine material at Resolute, as observed by Cook (1955, p. 244–247) and during the present investigation (see the section "Characteristics of Plugs and Plug Circles, Other characteristics: Discussion, 5b"). Consequently, initial freezing in the bowl-shaped thaw depression would tend to proceed from already frozen and rigid stony sides of the depression. Within the depression, the freezing and expansion of unfrozen fines whose freezing was delayed by the zero-curtain effect could result in the fines, while still somewhat plastic, being forced into overlying, still thawed soil by upward freezing from below the fines and/or by lateral stress due to a freezing front from bordering, already frozen gravel.

Characteristic plug fabrics, including the tendency for tabular stones to be on edge with long axis vertical or steeply inclined and for tabular stones immediately next to a plug to lie flat against it (see the section "Characteristics of Plugs and Plug Circles, Morphology, structure, and fabric: Review, 2–3"), combined with the generally compact nature of the main plug mass except near the frost or permafrost table, are consistent with a plastic upward plug movement. In the case of downward freezing from the surface, concentrations of freezing fines could also act as a piston on overlying levels and might cause differential surface heaving, but against an increasingly resistant frozen carapace as, for instance, in the case of Van Vliet-Lanoë's positive frost-susceptibility gradient (discussed earlier in this section). Eventually the upward-moving freezing front and the downward-moving front would meet, and freeze-up would be essentially complete except for freezing of unfrozen water at still lower temperatures.

Differential frost heaving and surfaceward seepage raises the question as to why thaw consolidation does not completely reverse the heaving. As cited earlier in the section "Soil circulation due to moisture-controlled changes in density," Hallet and Waddington (1991, p. 253) noted that "The factors responsible for this irreversibility and the resultant residual long-term motion of the soil remain somewhat of a mystery." They proposed that buoyancy of frost-susceptible soil during the thaw season could be a critical factor.

Possible factors include:

1. Buoyancy, as cited above, accelerated by surfaceward seepage.

2. Preservation of vesicles released during thawing of plugs (see the section "Characteristics of Plugs and Plug Circles, Morphology, structure, and fabric: Discussion, 2b"). A similar volume-maintenance effect has been cited for formerly ice-filled, droplike voids in N-circles (Semmel, 1969, p. 5).

3. Thawing of ice lenses leaving a somewhat expanded, loose soil structure (Williams and Smith, 1989, p. 137; White and Williams, 1994), even though thaw consolidation can reduce the effect significantly (cf. Williams and Smith, 1989, p. 138–141).

4. An absolute increase in volume of frost-susceptible fines by soil-translocation processes and by in-situ weathering of coarser particles (see the section "Characteristics of Plugs and Plug Circles, Constitution: Discussion, 1–7").

Whatever the details, it is concluded that plugs can be initiated, rise in the soil profile, and appear at the surface as plug circles as a result of differential frost heaving involving both upward and downward freezing of moisture-rich fines and incorporated coarser material to which more fines were being added over time. It is also concluded that surfaceward seepage is a critical companion process that helps to explain the location of many occurrences.

Problems. Possible difficulties exist with the hypothesis that plugs and plug circles originate by differential frost heaving, facilitated in places by surfaceward seepage.

1. The reason for the tendency of average pattern size in a given area to be rather uniform is not necessarily obvious. In the Resolute area, Nichols (1953, p. 275) reported "frost mounds" (clearly plug circles) 30 to more than 90 cm (1 to >3 ft.) in diameter; Cook (1956, p. 10) cited an average diameter of 38 cm (15 in.) with 82% of the 400 circles counted "falling within the model group." The range of values was not specified but "in isolated positions" the diameters averaged 30 cm (12 in.). Subsequently Cook (1959, p. 74) cited a diameter range of 20 to 100 cm and noted that the circles tended to be isolated but that they also occur in groups. The upper limit accords with my observations of undoubted plug circles, but the lower limit is 5 cm or less. In part, circle diameter is a function of stage of development in that plugs tend to have a blunt, somewhat conical top with the diameter increasing until the maximum cylindrical diameter is reached. On average, this may be close to the 38 cm cited by Cook, perhaps 40 to 50 cm. In my experience the largest plug S-circles and plug S-semicircles tend to occur in a high-moisture environment, which is also where they appear to be transitional to RB S-circles and closely related to them (see the section "Characteristics of Plugs and Plug Circles, Pattern: Review, 2").

Accounting for uniformity in pattern size is a challenging question in hypotheses other than those dependent on the regularity of contraction cracking (whether frost, permafrost, or desiccation cracking) or hypotheses based on convection or soil circulation. For the latter, the analogy with free convection becomes, in itself, an attractive supporting argument. Explanations not involving the above situations tend to focus on self-regulating processes such as mutual accommodation by radial freezing forces (cf. Conrad, 1946), which may or may not be present depending on the orientation of the freezing front. The even border of most plug circles (as opposed to those with a prominent stony ring) argues against the effectiveness of radial forces in producing uniform pattern size. Rather, expansion of plug circles accords better with heaving of fines-rich soil emerging from depth as plug circles of increasing diameter as their usually somewhat conical top penetrates overlying soil. A tendency for uniformity of size in an area of well-developed circles probably reflects uniformity of conditions—soil, moisture, temperature gradients, and depth of effective freezing and thawing. However, circle size can be quite different in nearby forms, and merging forms are not uncommon. Hallet and Waddington (1991, p. 273) indicated that diapirism has its own natural length scale in being proportional to thickness of a fines layer at depth, which leads to the conclusion that ". . . diapir spacings 1 to 2 m apart would be expected to form from a buoyant basal layer about 0.2 m thick. Such diapir spacings are similar to those of incipient sorted circles observed by the authors in western Spitsbergen and to ring-bordered sorted circles and the larger plugs [plug circles] observed by Washburn (1991) in the Canadian Arctic."

2. Plug movement requires thawed soil. Several studies have inferred that movement of plugs is the upward movement ("squeezing") of thawed soil, the primary evidence being the fabric and columnar shape of plugs (Cook, 1956, p. 17; Washburn, 1950, p. 41; 1956, p. 844). Such evidence does not support an origin by differential frost heaving but neither does it conflict where (1) lateral freezing fronts from bordering gravel can exert stress on still-mobile plug soil and lead to its upward movement if not inhibited by resistance of overlying soil, (2) basal freezing and heaving of plug soil can result in both the plug soil and any overlying unfrozen soil being forced differentially upward, and (3) plug fabric might merely reflect subsequent reorientation of stones and soil deformation resulting

from either freezing, frost jacking, thaw collapse, or volume changes associated with wetting or drying. Without detailed analysis, plug fabrics may not be a reliable criterion of plug emplacement in either a thawed or frozen mode or both (see the somewhat similar problem in "Soil circulation due to moisture-controlled changes in density, Problems, 4, Note"). The same problem may be applicable to some "mud boils," which in places may be comparable or identical to plug circles.

3. Plugs are most clearly structured where surrounded by openwork gravel. Where the adjacent soil is finer grained, the tendency for differential frost heaving might well be reduced. Variations in grain size, moisture, and seepage stress could all contribute to significant differences in heaving between a plug and bordering soil that might not be immediately apparent. Moreover, subcenters of activity in the central areas of some patterned ground (Figs. 40, 59, 64) suggest the possiblility of similar but less apparent occurrences in plugs themselves.

PATTERN EVOLUTION

As noted in the section "Terminology—patterned ground," plug S-circles lack the bulgy, ringlike stony border that characterizes RB S-circles. However, as discussed earlier in the section "Transitional Patterned-Ground Forms," some plug S-circles show transitions to other kinds of patterned ground, especially S-nets, and less certainly to RB S-circles. Forms intermediate between debris islands and RB S-circles have been reported from the highlands of Iceland (Schunke, 1975, Abb. 9) and observed by Bernard Hallet in Spitsbergen (personal communication, 1995).

Three propositions may be considered. As proposed in the section "Differential frost heaving and surfaceward seepage," (1) differential heaving is basic to the origin of plugs and plug circles, (2) lower soil densities at depth than higher in the profile can lead to upward soil movement that may be reinforced by a sufficiently strong hydraulic gradient to cause surfaceward seepage of fines, and (3) perhaps plugs can evolve into some other types of patterned ground including RB S-circles.

If proposition (1) is accepted as reasonable, proposition (3) suggests that buoyancy effects may not be the primary cause of classical RB S-circles of the Spitsbergen type, a proposition consistent with Hallet and Waddington's (1991, p. 270–271) conclusion, discussed earlier in the section "Soil circulation due to moisture-controlled changes in density," that the effective Rayleigh number required does not permit sustainable circulation in previously unpatterned active layers. These authors allow for intermittent diapirism of fine-grained soil (Hallet and Waddington, 1991, p. 271–273). Proposition (3) allows for the possibility that plugs may reach a concentration or critical volume of fines or may achieve some self-induced change conducive to soil circulation, whereby plugs become a protoform of well-developed RB S-circles (Butrym et al., 1964, p. 22–29; Dżułyński, 1963; Dżułyński, 1966, p. 18–19; Washburn, 1989, p. 953–954). Thus although many investigators accept RB S-circles as originating by soil circulation, the circulation may not be the immediate cause but an evolutionary development in a plug pattern where soil circulation eventually becomes the primary process, whereas soil diapirism is essentially limited to a simple soil overturn and/or incorporation of "new," previously uncirculated soil without requiring recirculation of soil within the same form.

Intermediate forms between S-circles and S-nets or S-polygons were observed by Gripp (1927, p. 9), and a progression to S-polygons was inferred by Chambers (1967, p. 20), among others. However, a distinction between polygons (straight borders with sharp angles) as opposed to nets (irregular, somewhat rounded borders) is not always made, and perhaps most reports of intermediate forms refer to a circle-net progression of forms as observed by Gripp rather than a circle-net-polygon sequence.

With respect to plug circles, it seems clear that transitional forms occur that suggest an evolutionary sequence. It is tempting to speculate that plug S-circles can evolve to RB S-circles, either directly or through S-nets; furthermore that they may evolve through S-nets to S-polygons as a result of increasing crowding on a near-horizontal surface and to stripes on a slope. If so, most patterned ground, except for contraction-crack patterns, may basically begin as a plug initiated by differential frost heaving and surfaceward seepage.

In summary, it can be reasonably concluded from the Cornwallis Island observations on pattern evolution that some plug S-circles are transitional to S-nets and perhaps RB S-circles. It seems probable, judging from the literature and my observations, that most well-developed, straight-sided polygons reflect contraction cracking, but it is conceivable that continued crowding of net patterns might produce some truly straight-sided polygons. An evolutionary transition of sorted patterns to nonsorted ones by weathering and comminution of stony borders was visualized by Huxley and Odell (1924, p. 228), and the relation of some Resolute plugs to disintegrating bedrock and in-situ disintegration of clasts supports this possibility for easily weathered stony borders.

Whether or not such an evolution is borne out for plug forms, the conclusion seems warranted that they can be transitional to other varieties, whether in surficial appearance only and nongenetic or perhaps truly genetic with respect to process.

Finally, the evidence argues for the importance of plugs and plug circles as a basic and widespread form of patterned ground in permafrost environments. Plug forms in beach gravel, miscellaneous deposits, and disintegrating bedrock, summarized as to overall characteristics and evaluated with respect to hypotheses of origin, lead to the conclusion that plugs and plug circles originate by differential frost heaving, with surfaceward seepage determining the location of many occurrences.

SUMMARY AND CONCLUSIONS

Plugs and plug circles as patterned-ground forms

Plug circles are a circular variety of patterned ground characterized by fines-rich soil that continues to depth as a plug—a subsurface cylindrical or more irregular form. Plugs may also terminate before reaching the surface. (Formal definitions are given in the section "Terminology—patterned ground.") Plug forms (i.e., plug circles, plugs, and plug semicircles) may be very stony or essentially free of stones. Plug circles can be sorted or nonsorted, but if sorted they are commonly even-bordered (i.e., they lack a ringlike, raised stony border >5 cm high). Plugs commonly originate in a fines-rich deposit at depth and are underlain by concentrations of ice at or near the permafrost table.

Cornwallis Island occurrences

In the Resolute area plugs and plug circles are very well developed in the prevailing carbonate terrain, particularly on impure varieties where weathering leaves abundant fines. They form in diverse unconsolidated deposits, including gravel, diamictons, and disintegrating bedrock. They can develop within 20 yr in disturbed soil, but most are very much older. Radiocarbon ages of shells from plugs range from some 4000 to 5000 ^{14}C B.P. at altitudes of 5 to 15 m, to 9140 ± 50 ^{14}C B.P. at an altitude of 85 m ± 1 m (nonplug shell occurrences range up to 9790 ^{14}C B.P. and in altitude up to 117 ± 3 m) (Appendix C).

Observations were also made elsewhere as opportunity offered, but they, too, were mostly in soils associated with the widespread limestone and dolomite bedrock of the island. An unusual departure was the presence of small, well-developed pluglike patterns disrupting shale bedrock near the west coast (see the section "Occurrences in Disintegrating Bedrock, Other observations, Gypsum diapir").

Observations in the Resolute area where the most detailed observations were made show that

1. Plug forms in beach gravel tend to be aligned parallel to contours, and in places occur as pinnacles on a plug ridge;
2. Closely spaced, aligned plug forms in gravel can form more or less parallel rows that have a slight, but marked and more or less continuous, upslope-facing relief, formed by adjacent plug circles or semicircles;
3. In places plug forms occur preferentially along permafrost cracks;
4. Some plugs are connected by subsurface necks of predominantly fine soil;
5. Plug forms tend to thaw deeper than adjacent coarser soil, resulting in a bowl-shaped thaw depression in the frost table and probably in the permafrost table;
6. At depth, elongate stones in plugs tend to dip steeply, and tabular stones tend to be on edge with flat surfaces parallel to plug sides; and
7. Fines tend to move to depth and downslope in the soil profile, accumulating where further movement is slowed or inhibited.

Regional distribution

Plug forms are widely developed in Arctic Canada, including Devon, Prince Patrick, and Victoria Islands. They also occur in Greenland, Spitsbergen, and the Eurasian Arctic. Most or all of these reported occurrences are in permafrost environments, and permafrost may be an essential condition. It would be surprising if comparable occurrences were not also present in many other present permafrost environments, including Antarctic, subantarctic, and possibly alpine regions, and also as fossil features in some former permafrost environments.

Origin

Evidence provided by (1) relation of plug forms to site-specific environmental factors, such as the nature of the bedrock, soil, slope, temperature, moisture, and any vegetation; (2) numerous excavations; (3) laboratory analyses; and (4) review of possibly applicable hypotheses of origin leads to the conclusion that plugs and plug circles originate by differential frost heaving with surfaceward seepage being an important companion process that explains the location of many occurrences. This hypothesis includes the possibility that soil may be displaced upward in a fluid, plastic, or frozen condition by freezing-induced stress.

The differential heaving can be associated with freezing fronts moving downward from the surface, upward from a frost or permafrost table, and laterally from colder horizons. Water infiltrating frozen ground at depth and refreezing would act as a piston tending to push up and/or shoulder aside overlying mobile soil.

Thawing following differential heaving would not generally result in total collapse of the frost-heaved soil. Some soil would tend to remain displaced upward as the result of (1) a somewhat expanded soil structure left by thawing ice lenses and preservation of some vesicles associated with freezing and thawing, (2) the adherence of some heaved or otherwise displaced soil to adjacent more stable soil, and (3) the effect of any sustained buoyancy force present. Given incremental heaving over time, locally emphasized by differential accumulations of fines and moisture, high points on an accumulation of fines would tend to rise in the active layer as plugs; if plugs breach the ground surface they become plug circles. Any local thinning of the active layer by erosion or lateral spreading of a circle at the surface would be compensated by thawing of underlying permafrost, thereby restoring the thickness of the active layer and providing additional soil that could become subject to differential frost heaving and surfaceward seepage.

Transitional forms

Transitions from plug circles to other types of patterned ground strongly suggest that plugs can evolve into the other types, including sorted nets, and perhaps some ring-bordered sorted circles and polygons. Further evidence is required to establish if the transitions are truly continuous and, if so, whether they depend on conditions primarily affecting a purely descriptive classification of forms or whether a quite different genetic process is critically involved as supported by evidence for the basic role of soil circulation in some RB S-circles, including the classical Spitsbergen occurrences.

Significance

Plug circles constitute a little-studied, basic variety of patterned ground with transitional and possibly evolutionary aspects leading to some other varieties of patterned ground. An understanding of plug forms may be fundamental to understanding diverse other forms of patterned ground and more generally to understanding self-organization in freezing and thawing soils. At the very least, plug forms provide important information on soil processes and environmental conditions of both scientific and practical importance.

TABLE 1. PLUG AT RADSTOCK BAY, DEVON ISLAND, N.W.T., GRAIN-SIZE ANALYSES, NONTRUNCATED. MODIFIED FROM BUNTING AND JACKSON, 1970, TABLES 1–2, p. 202*

Sp. No.	Depth (cm)	Specimen Name	Matrix Name	Bulk Density
7	15–25	Silty$_{16}$-clayey$_{19}$-sandy$_{22}$ gravel$_{42}$	Silty$_{28}$-clayey$_{33}$ sand$_{38}$	
9	25–30	Silty$_{17}$-clayey$_{17}$-sandy$_{17}$ gravel$_{49}$	Silty$_{33}$ clay$_{34}$-sand$_{34}$	
10	30–35	Sandy$_{11}$-silty$_{16}$-clayey$_{17}$ gravel$_{56}$	Sandy$_{24}$ silt$_{37}$-clay$_{39}$	
11	40–45	Sandy$_{14}$-clayey$_{15}$-silty$_{16}$ gravel$_{54}$	Sandy$_{31}$ clay$_{33}$-silt$_{36}$	
Combined depths	15–45	Sandy$_{16}$-silty$_{16}$-clayey$_{17}$ gravel$_{50}$	Sandy$_{32}$ silt$_{34}$-clay$_{35}$	1.61

*The sand/silt and silt/clay boundaries are 0.05 mm and 0.002 mm respectively as cited by the authors. Consequently these grain-size boundaries, compared to those for the Modified Wentworth scale (0.062 and 0.004, respectively) adopted for the Resolute specimens (cf. Washburn et al., 1963), result in the Devon Island specimens showing somewhat lower silt and clay percentages than would be the case for Resolute specimens. The difference does not significantly affect a general comparison.

TABLE 2. PE 85-8 (SPS. 85-8-8C1–8D, -8F–8H2, -9B–9C), GRAIN-SIZE ANALYSES, TRUNCATED AT 8 MM. EXPERIMENTAL SITE C, RESOLUTE, CORNWALLIS ISLAND, N.W.T.

Location PE 85-8	Depth (cm)	Specimen	Specimen name	Matrix name	Weight (<8 mm) (g)	Total weight (g)
Plug	0–8	85-8-8C1	Clayey$_{8}$-sandy$_{14}$-gravelly$_{20}$ silt$_{57}$	Clayey$_{10}$-sandy$_{18}$ silt$_{72}$	687.7	1,202.4
Plug	0–8	85-8-8C2	Clayey$_{11}$-sandy$_{20}$-gravelly$_{20}$ silt$_{50}$	Clayey$_{14}$-sandy$_{25}$ silt$_{62}$	1,136.6	1,616.1
Plug	8–16	85-8-8D	Clayey$_{8}$-sandy$_{14}$-gravelly$_{26}$ silt$_{52}$	Clayey$_{11}$-sandy$_{19}$ silt$_{70}$	647.8	1,257.8
Plug outer part	24–32	85-8-8F	Clayey$_{7}$-sandy$_{13}$-gravelly$_{36}$ silt$_{45}$	Clayey$_{10}$-sandy$_{20}$ silt$_{70}$	478.3	1,028.4
Plug core	24–32	85-8-8G	Clayey$_{9}$-sandy$_{13}$-gravelly$_{18}$ silt$_{60}$	Clayey$_{12}$-sandy$_{16}$ silt$_{73}$	690.1	1,286.5
Plug core	32–50	85-8-8H1	Clayey$_{9}$-sandy$_{12}$-gravelly$_{16}$ silt$_{64}$	Clayey$_{10}$-sandy$_{14}$ silt$_{76}$	634.3	1,118.1
Plug core	32–50	85-8-8H2	Clayey$_{10}$-gravelly$_{15}$-sandy$_{18}$ silt$_{57}$	Clayey$_{12}$-sandy$_{21}$ silt$_{67}$	163.2	297.8
Probably below and outside plug base. 11% ice (by wt.)	50–70	85-8-9B	Clayey$_{5}$-sandy$_{11}$-silty$_{31}$ gravel$_{53}$	Clayey$_{10}$-sandy$_{24}$ silt$_{66}$	400.2	1,052.2
Below plug base. 24% ice (by wt.)	70–80	85-8-9C	Clayey$_{7}$-sandy$_{11}$-gravelly$_{19}$ silt$_{62}$	Clayey$_{9}$-sandy$_{14}$ silt$_{77}$	255.9	1018.6

TABLE 3. PE 89-1 (SPS. 89-7-17A–17R), GRAIN-SIZE ANALYSES, TRUNCATED AT 8 MM. EXPERIMENTAL SITE C, RESOLUTE, CORNWALLIS ISLAND, N.W.T.

Location PE 89-1	Depth (cm)	Specimen	Specimen name	Matrix name	Weight (<8 mm) (g)	Total weight (g)
Plug upslope side	0–5	89-7-17A	Clayey$_6$-sandy$_{23}$-gravelly$_{24}$ silt$_{47}$	Clayey$_7$-sandy$_{30}$ silt$_{63}$	213.0	270.5
Plug including core	0–5	89-7-17B	Clayey$_7$-gravelly$_{11}$-sandy$_{31}$ silt$_{51}$	Clayey$_8$-sandy$_{35}$ silt$_{57}$	218.8	419.4
Plug downslope side	0–5	89-7-17C	Gravelly$_9$-clayey$_{10}$-sandy$_{21}$ silt$_{60}$	Clayey$_{11}$-sandy$_{23}$ silt$_{66}$	156.2	355.6
Plug upslope side	5–10	89-7-17D	Clayey$_8$-sandy$_{20}$-gravelly$_{30}$ silt$_{41}$	Clayey$_{12}$-sandy$_{29}$ silt$_{59}$	326.5	407.6
Plug including core	5–10	89-7-17E	Clayey$_5$-sandy$_{26}$ gravel$_{33}$-silt$_{36}$	Clayey$_8$-sandy$_{38}$ silt$_{54}$	212.5	371.0
Plug downslope side	5–10	89-7-17F	Clayey$_5$-sandy$_{16}$ silt$_{38}$-gravel$_{42}$	Clayey$_8$-sandy$_{27}$ silt$_{65}$	154.3	587.7
Plug upslope side	10–20	89-7-17G	Clayey$_8$-sandy$_{20}$ gravel$_{35}$-silt$_{38}$	Clayey$_8$-sandy$_{30}$ silt$_{58}$	316.7	704.3
Plug	10–20	89-7-17H	Clayey$_3$-sandy$_{20}$-silty$_{23}$ gravel$_{54}$	Clayey$_7$-sandy$_{42}$ silt$_{51}$	292.8	780.6
Plug downslope side	10–20	89-7-17I	Clayey$_5$-sandy$_{19}$ silt$_{37}$-gravel$_{40}$	Clayey$_8$-sandy$_{31}$ silt$_{61}$	306.0	1,398.6
Plug upslope side	20–30	89-7-17J	Clayey$_7$-gravelly$_{14}$-sandy$_{26}$ silt$_{53}$	Clayey$_8$-sandy$_{21}$ silt$_{61}$	472.1	972.0
Plug	20–30	89-7-17K	Clayey$_2$-sandy$_{14}$-silty$_{16}$ gravel$_{67}$	Clayey$_7$-sandy$_{43}$ silt$_{49}$	344.4	1,070.5
Plug downslope side	20–30	89-7-17L	Clayey$_7$-gravelly$_{20}$-sandy$_{27}$ silt$_{45}$	Clayey$_9$-sandy$_{34}$ silt$_{57}$	430.5	829.4
Plug upslope side	30–40	89-7-17M	Clayey$_5$-sandy$_{19}$ gravel$_{37}$-silt$_{38}$	Clayey$_9$-sandy$_{31}$ silt$_{61}$	374.5	742.3
Plug	30–40	89-7-17N	Clayey$_8$-sandy$_{22}$-gravelly$_{22}$ silt$_{48}$	Clayey$_{10}$-sandy$_{28}$ silt$_{62}$	465.9	980.1
Plug center	30–40	89-7-17O	Clayey$_8$-gravelly$_{12}$-sandy$_{23}$ silt$_{58}$	Clayey$_9$-sandy$_{26}$ silt$_{66}$	408.4	1,152.8
Plug downslope side	30–40	89-7-17P	Clayey$_5$-sandy$_{18}$ gravel$_{36}$-silt$_{41}$	Clayey$_8$-sandy$_{28}$ silt$_{64}$	481.4	985.1
Openwork gravel	40–50	89-7-17Q	Clayey$_5$-gravelly$_{27}$-sandy$_{30}$ silt$_{39}$	Clayey$_7$-sandy$_{41}$ silt$_{53}$	431.4	1,230.1
Plug	45–50	89-7-17R	Gravelly$_6$-clayey$_7$-sandy$_{28}$ silt$_{58}$	Clayey$_8$-sandy$_{30}$ silt$_{62}$	613.8	1,196.4

TABLE 4. PE 90-1 (SP. 90-8-24) AND PE 90-2 (SP. 90-9-3A), GRAIN-SIZE ANALYSES, NONTRUNCATED. EXPERIMENTAL SITE C AND VICINITY, RESOLUTE, CORNWALLIS ISLAND, N.W.T.

Location PE 90-1 PE 90-2	Depth (cm)	Specimen	Specimen name	Matrix name	Total weight (g)	Plastic limit (%)	Liquid limit (%)	Bulk density (g/cm^3)
Plug 1	0–42	90-8-24	Clayey$_2$-silty$_{13}$-sandy$_{17}$ gravel$_{69}$	Clayey$_6$-silty$_{41}$ sand$_{53}$	7,833.8	19	21	2.07
Plug 2	0–38	90-9-3A	Clayey$_2$-silty$_{17}$-sandy$_{20}$ gravel$_{61}$	Clayey$_6$-silty$_{43}$ sand$_{50}$	3,628.2	20	26	1.99
Average	0–40		Clayey$_2$-silty$_{15}$-sandy$_{18}$ gravel$_{65}$	Clayey$_6$-silty$_{42}$ sand$_{52}$		19.5	23.5	2.03

TABLE 5. PE 90-1 (SP. 90-8-24) AND PE 90-2 (SP. 90-9-3A), GRAIN-SIZE ANALYSES, TRUNCATED AT 8 MM. EXPERIMENTAL SITE C AND VICINITY, RESOLUTE, CORNWALLIS ISLAND, N.W.T.

Location PE 90-1 PE 90-2	Depth (cm)	Specimen	Specimen name	Matrix name	Weight (<8 mm) (g)	Plastic limit (%)	Liquid limit (%)	Bulk density* (g/cm^3)
Plug 1	0–42	90-8-24	Clayey$_5$-gravelly$_{29}$-silty$_{29}$ sand$_{38}$	Clayey$_6$-silty$_{41}$ sand$_{53}$	3,431.1	19	21	2.07
Plug 2	0–38	90-9-3A	Clayey$_4$-silty$_{28}$ sand$_{33}$-gravel$_{35}$	Clayey$_6$-silty$_{43}$ sand$_{50}$	2,171.8	20	26	1.99
Average	0–40		Clayey$_4$-silty$_{29}$ gravel$_{32}$-sand$_{35}$	Clayey$_6$-silty$_{42}$ sand$_{52}$				

*Nontruncated.

TABLE 6. PE 90-1 (SP. 90-8-24) AND PE 90-2 (SP. 90-9-3A), NONTRUNCATED, PLUNGE OF LONG AXIS >1.5 INTERMEDIATE AXIS OF STONES. EXPERIMENTAL SITE C AND VICINITY, RESOLUTE, CORNWALLIS ISLAND, N.W.T.

PE 90-1 (SP. 90-8-24)

Location PE 90-1	Stones	Plunge of long axis in degrees 0–9	10–19	20–29	30–39	40–49	50–59	60–69	70–79	80–90	Totals
Upper third	Number	5	4	4	1	1	4	1	5	0	25
	Percent	20	16	16	4	4	16	4	20	0	100
Middle third	Number	1	3	3	5	5	4	4	7	3	35
	Percent	3	9	9	14	14	11	11	20	9	100
Lower third	Number	1	0	1	3	0	0	0	3	0	8
	Percent	12	0	13	38	0	0	0	38	0	101
Total	Number	7	7	8	9	6	8	5	15	3	68
	Percent	10	10	12	13	9	12	7	22	4	99

Note: Plug diameters at top and bottom, respectively, were 25 and 27 cm. A uniform diameter of 26 cm was assumed for analyses of stone distribution.

PE 90-2 (SP. 90-9-3A)

Location PE 90-2	Stones	Plunge of long axis in degrees 0–9	10–19	20–29	30–39	40–49	50–59	60–69	70–79	80–90	Totals
Upper third	Number	0	0	0	0	0	0	1	2	0	3
	Percent	0	0	0	0	0	0	33	67	0	100
Middle third	Number	1	1	0	0	0	4	8	9	2	25
	Percent	4	4	0	0	0	16	32	36	8	100
Lower third	Number	1	0	0	2	2	2	10	12	8	37
	Percent	3	0	0	5	5	5	27	32	22	99
Total	Number	2	1	0	2	2	6	19	23	10	65
	Percent	3	2	0	3	3	9	29	35	15	99

TABLE 7. PE 95-1 (SPS. 95-8-20-1A–1I), GRAIN-SIZE ANALYSES, NONTRUNCATED. EXPERIMENTAL SITE C, RESOLUTE, CORNWALLIS ISLAND, N.W.T.

Location PE 95-1	Depth (cm)	Specimen*	Specimen name	Matrix name	Total weight (g)	Bulk density (g/cm^3)
Plug	0–20	95-8-20-1A	Clayey$_2$-sandy$_8$-silty$_{15}$ gravel$_{76}$	Clayey$_7$-sandy$_{33}$ silt$_{60}$	2,427.8	
Plug	0–20	95-8-20-1B	Clayey$_3$-sandy$_9$-silty$_{20}$ gravel$_{68}$	Clayey$_8$-sandy$_{29}$ silt$_{62}$	2,358.1	
Plug	0–20	95-8-20-1C	Clayey$_3$-sandy$_{11}$-silty$_{24}$ gravel$_{63}$	Clayey$_7$-sandy$_{29}$ silt$_{64}$	3,029.4	
Plug	20–40	95-8-20-1D	Clayey$_3$-sandy$_6$-silty$_{23}$ gravel$_{68}$	Clayey$_8$-sandy$_{18}$ silt$_{73}$	1,982.6	
Plug	20–40	95-8-20-1E	Clayey$_2$-sandy$_9$-silty$_{16}$ gravel$_{73}$	Clayey$_8$-sandy$_{32}$ silt$_{60}$	1,366.1	
Plug	20–40	95-8-20-1F	Clayey$_3$-sandy$_{10}$-silty$_{23}$ gravel$_{65}$	Clayey$_8$-sandy$_{28}$ silt$_{64}$	1,100.8	
Plug	40–60	95-8-20-1G	Clayey$_2$-sandy$_6$-silty$_{13}$ gravel$_{79}$	Clayey$_8$-sandy$_{30}$ silt$_{62}$	2,092.4	
Plug	40–60	95-8-20-1H	Clayey$_1$-sandy$_4$-silty$_{10}$ gravel$_{84}$	Clayey$_7$-sandy$_{28}$ silt$_{65}$	1,654.5	
Plug	40–60	95-8-20-1I	Clayey$_1$-sandy$_6$-silty$_{14}$ gravel$_{79}$	Clayey$_6$-sandy$_{26}$ silt$_{66}$	2,133.5	
Average			Clayey$_2$-sandy$_8$-silty$_{17}$ gravel$_{73}$	Clayey$_7$-sandy$_{28}$ silt$_{64}$	18,145.2	1.49

* Specimen locations are given in Figure 32.

TABLE 8. PE 95-1 (SPS. 95-8-20-1A–1I), GRAIN-SIZE ANALYSES, TRUNCATED AT 8 MM. EXPERIMENTAL SITE C, RESOLUTE, CORNWALLIS ISLAND, N.W.T.

Location PE 95-1	Depth (cm)	Specimen*	Specimen name	Matrix name	Weight (<8 mm) (g)
Plug	0–20	95-8-20-1A	Clayey$_{4}$-sandy$_{21}$ gravel$_{37}$-silt$_{38}$	Clayey$_{7}$-sandy$_{33}$ silt$_{60}$	927.2
Plug	0–20	95-8-20-1B	Clayey$_{6}$-sandy$_{22}$-gravelly$_{25}$ silt$_{47}$	Clayey$_{8}$-sandy$_{29}$ silt$_{62}$	992.8
Plug	0–20	95-8-20-1C	Clayey$_{5}$-gravelly$_{22}$-sandy$_{23}$ silt$_{50}$	Clayey$_{7}$-sandy$_{29}$ silt$_{64}$	1,425.6
Plug	20–40	95-8-20-1D	Clayey$_{7}$-sandy$_{15}$-gravelly$_{21}$ silt$_{57}$	Clayey$_{8}$-sandy$_{18}$ silt$_{73}$	804.5
Plug	20–40	95-8-20-1E	Clayey$_{6}$-sandy$_{22}$-gravelly$_{32}$ silt$_{41}$	Clayey$_{8}$-sandy$_{32}$ silt$_{60}$	538.4
Plug	20–40	95-8-20-1F	Clayey$_{6}$-sandy$_{20}$-gravelly$_{28}$ silt$_{46}$	Clayey$_{8}$-sandy$_{28}$ silt$_{64}$	538.7
Plug	40–60	95-8-20-1G	Clayey$_{5}$-sandy$_{18}$ gravel$_{38}$-silt$_{38}$	Clayey$_{8}$-sandy$_{30}$ silt$_{62}$	705.9
Plug	40–60	95-8-20-1H	Clayey$_{4}$-sandy$_{18}$ gravel$_{38}$-silt$_{40}$	Clayey$_{7}$-sandy$_{28}$ silt$_{65}$	413.2
Plug	40–60	95-8-20-1I	Clayey$_{4}$-sandy$_{18}$-gravelly$_{36}$ silt$_{42}$	Clayey$_{6}$-sandy$_{26}$ silt$_{66}$	700.1
Average			Clayey$_{5}$-sandy$_{20}$-gravelly$_{31}$ silt$_{44}$	Clayey$_{7}$-sandy$_{28}$ silt$_{64}$	7,046.4

* Specimen locations are given in Figure 32.

TABLE 9. PE 95-2 (SPS. 95-8-20-2A–2I), GRAIN-SIZE ANALYSES, NONTRUNCATED. VICINITY EXPERIMENTAL SITE C, RESOLUTE, CORNWALLIS ISLAND, N.W.T.

Location PE 95-2	Depth (cm)	Specimen*	Specimen name	Matrix name	Total weight (g)	Bulk density (g/cm^3)
Plug	0–14	95-8-20-2A	Clayey$_{3}$-sandy$_{7}$-silty$_{16}$ gravel$_{74}$	Clayey$_{11}$-sandy$_{28}$ silt$_{61}$	1,225.5	
Plug	0–14	95-8-20-2B	Clayey$_{3}$-sandy$_{14}$-silty$_{25}$ gravel$_{58}$	Clayey$_{8}$-sandy$_{33}$ silt$_{59}$	576.7	
Plug	0–14	95-8-20-2C	Clayey$_{4}$-sandy$_{14}$-silty$_{28}$ gravel$_{54}$	Clayey$_{8}$-sandy$_{32}$ silt$_{61}$	506.5	
Plug	14–28	95-8-20-2D	Clayey$_{2}$-sandy$_{9}$-silty$_{13}$ gravel$_{76}$	Clayey$_{8}$-sandy$_{38}$ silt$_{54}$	741.3	
Plug	14–28	95-8-20-2E	Clayey$_{3}$-sandy$_{11}$-silty$_{20}$ gravel$_{66}$	Clayey$_{8}$-sandy$_{33}$ silt$_{59}$	931.5	
Plug	14–28	95-8-20-2F	Clayey$_{4}$-sandy$_{19}$-silty$_{27}$ gravel$_{51}$	Clayey$_{8}$-sandy$_{38}$ silt$_{54}$	1,163.9	
Plug	28–42	95-8-20-2G	Clayey$_{2}$-sandy$_{10}$-silty$_{16}$ gravel$_{73}$	Clayey$_{7}$-sandy$_{35}$ silt$_{58}$	645.9	
Plug	28–42	95-8-20-2H	Clayey$_{3}$-sandy$_{13}$-silty$_{22}$ gravel$_{62}$	Clayey$_{8}$-sandy$_{34}$ silt$_{58}$	993.9	
Plug	28–42	95-8-20-2I	Clayey$_{2}$-sandy$_{12}$-silty$_{19}$ gravel$_{67}$	Clayey$_{7}$-sandy$_{36}$ silt$_{57}$	1,449.0	
Average			Clayey$_{3}$-sandy$_{12}$-silty$_{20}$ gravel$_{65}$	Clayey$_{8}$-sandy$_{34}$ silt$_{58}$	8,234.2	1.78

*Specimen locations are given in Figure 33.

TABLE 10. PE 95-2 (SPS. 95-8-20-2A–2I), GRAIN-SIZE ANALYSES, TRUNCATED AT 8 MM. VICINITY EXPERIMENTAL SITE C, RESOLUTE, CORNWALLIS ISLAND, N.W.T.

Location PE 95-2	Depth (cm)	Specimen*	Specimen name	Matrix name	Weight (<8 mm) (g)
Plug	0–14	95-8-20-2A	Clayey$_7$-sandy$_{18}$ gravel$_{37}$-silt$_{39}$	Clayey$_{11}$-sandy$_{28}$ silt$_{61}$	496.8
Plug	0–14	95-8-20-2B	Clayey$_6$-gravelly$_{23}$-sandy$_{25}$ silt$_{45}$	Clayey$_8$-sandy$_{33}$ silt$_{59}$	315.1
Plug	0–14	95-8-20-2C	Clayey$_6$-gravelly$_{17}$-sandy$_{26}$ silt$_{50}$	Clayey$_8$-sandy$_{32}$ silt$_{61}$	279.6
Plug	14–28	95-8-20-2D	Clayey$_4$-sandy$_{18}$-silty$_{25}$ gravel$_{53}$	Clayey$_8$-sandy$_{38}$ silt$_{54}$	374.8
Plug	14–28	95-8-20-2E	Clayey$_6$-sandy$_{23}$-gravelly$_{30}$ silt$_{42}$	Clayey$_8$-sandy$_{33}$ silt$_{59}$	447.0
Plug	14–28	95-8-20-2F	Clayey$_7$-gravelly$_{22}$-sandy$_{30}$ silt$_{42}$	Clayey$_8$-sandy$_{38}$ silt$_{54}$	734.5
Plug	28–42	95-8-20-2G	Clayey$_4$-sandy$_{21}$ silt$_{35}$-gravel$_{39}$	Clayey$_7$-sandy$_{35}$ silt$_{58}$	289.1
Plug	28–42	95-8-20-2H	Clayey$_6$-sandy$_{24}$-gravelly$_{29}$ silt$_{41}$	Clayey$_8$-sandy$_{34}$ silt$_{58}$	539.4
Plug	28–42	95-8-20-2I	Clayey$_5$-gravelly$_{24}$-sandy$_{27}$ silt$_{43}$	Clayey$_7$-sandy$_{36}$ silt$_{57}$	634.1
Average			Clayey$_6$-sandy$_{24}$-gravelly$_{30}$ silt$_{40}$	Clayey$_8$-sandy$_{34}$ silt$_{58}$	4,110.4

*Specimen locations are given in Figure 33.

TABLE 11. PE 95-3 (SPS. 95-8-21A–21I), GRAIN-SIZE ANALYSES, NONTRUNCATED. EXPERIMENTAL SITE C, RESOLUTE, CORNWALLIS ISLAND, N.W.T.

Location PE 95-3	Depth (cm)	Specimen*	Specimen name	Matrix name	Total weight (g)	Bulk density (g/cm^3)
Plug	0–15	95-8-21A	Clayey$_2$-sandy$_5$-silty$_{12}$ gravel$_{81}$	Clayey$_8$-sandy$_{27}$ silt$_{66}$	1,046.0	
Plug	0–15	95-8-21B	Clayey$_5$-sandy$_9$-silty$_{25}$ gravel$_{61}$	Clayey$_{12}$-sandy$_{23}$ silt$_{65}$	714.2	
Plug	0–15	95-8-21C	Clayey$_4$-sandy$_7$-silty$_{23}$ gravel$_{66}$	Clayey$_{12}$-sandy$_{21}$ silt$_{67}$	511.9	
Plug	15–25	95-8-21D	Clayey$_1$-sandy$_5$-silty$_9$ gravel$_{85}$	Clayey$_9$-sandy$_{32}$ silt$_{59}$	1,259.4	
Plug	15–25	95-8-21E	Clayey$_4$-sandy$_7$-silty$_{22}$ gravel$_{68}$	Clayey$_{12}$-sandy$_{20}$ silt$_{68}$	870.3	
Plug	15–25	95-8-21F	Clayey$_4$-sandy$_8$-silty$_{21}$ gravel$_{67}$	Clayey$_{13}$-sandy$_{23}$ silt$_{64}$	1,017.7	
Plug	25–40	95-8-21G	Clayey$_2$-sandy$_5$-silty$_{11}$ gravel$_{82}$	Clayey$_{11}$-sandy$_{26}$ silt$_{63}$	1,741.3	
Plug	25–40	95-8-21H	Clayey$_3$-sandy$_6$-silty$_{17}$ gravel$_{74}$	Clayey$_{10}$-sandy$_{24}$ silt$_{66}$	1,543.1	
Plug	25–40	95-8-21I	Clayey$_3$-sandy$_7$-silty$_{20}$ gravel$_{71}$	Clayey$_9$-sandy$_{24}$ silt$_{67}$	3,701.5	
Average			Clayey$_3$-sandy$_6$-silty$_{18}$ gravel$_{73}$	Clayey$_{11}$-sandy$_{24}$ silt$_{66}$	12,405.4	1.81

*Specimen locations are given in Figure 35.

TABLE 12. PE 95-3 (SPS. 95-8-21A–21I), GRAIN-SIZE ANALYSES, TRUNCATED AT 8 MM. EXPERIMENTAL SITE C, RESOLUTE, CORNWALLIS ISLAND, N.W.T.

Location PE 95-3	Depth (cm)	Specimen*	Specimen name	Matrix name	Weight <8 mm (g)
Plug	0–15	95-8-21A	$Clayey_4$-$sandy_{14}$-$silty_{34}$ $gravel_{49}$	$Clayey_8$-$sandy_{27}$ $silt_{66}$	384.7
Plug	0–15	95-8-21B	$Clayey_8$-$sandy_{16}$-$gravelly_{31}$ $silt_{45}$	$Clayey_{12}$-$sandy_{23}$ $silt_{65}$	400.3
Plug	0–15	95-8-21C	$Clayey_8$-$sandy_{15}$- $gravelly_{30}$ $silt_{47}$	$Clayey_{12}$-$sandy_{21}$ $silt_{67}$	247.0
Plug	15–25	95-8-21D	$Clayey_4$-$sandy_{13}$-$silty_{24}$ $gravel_{59}$	$Clayey_9$-$sandy_{32}$ $silt_{59}$	450.3
Plug	15–25	95-8-21E	$Clayey_7$-$sandy_{13}$-$gravelly_{38}$ $silt_{43}$	$Clayey_{12}$-$sandy_{20}$ $silt_{68}$	450.1
Plug	15–25	95-8-21F	$Clayey_9$-$sandy_{17}$-$gravelly_{28}$ $silt_{46}$	$Clayey_{13}$-$sandy_{23}$ $silt_{64}$	468.4
Plug	25–40	95-8-21G	$Clayey_6$-$sandy_{14}$-$silty_{35}$ $gravel_{45}$	$Clayey_{11}$-$sandy_{26}$ $silt_{63}$	564.3
Plug	25–40	95-8-21H	$Clayey_6$-$sandy_{15}$ $gravel_{37}$-$silt_{41}$	$Clayey_{10}$-$sandy_{24}$ $silt_{66}$	649.9
Plug	25–40	95-8-21I	$Clayey_6$-$sandy_{17}$-$gravelly_{28}$ $silt_{48}$	$Clayey_9$-$sandy_{24}$ $silt_{67}$	1,521.6
Average			$Clayey_7$-$sandy_{15}$ $gravel_{38}$-$silt_{40}$	$Clayey_{11}$-$sandy_{24}$ $silt_{66}$	5,136.6

*Specimen locations are given in Figure 35.

TABLE 13. PE 81-1 (SPS. 81-8-19A–19J), GRAIN-SIZE ANALYSES, NONTRUNCATED.* ABOUT 350 M SOUTHWEST OF NORTH TRANSMITTER STATION, RESOLUTE, CORNWALLIS ISLAND, N.W.T.

Location PE 81-1	Depth (cm)	Specimen†	Specimen name	Matrix name
Plug	10–15	81-8-19A	$Clayey_2$-$gravelly_{19}$-$silty_{37}$ $sand_{42}$	$Clayey_2$-$silty_{46}$ $sand_{52}$
Plug	20–25	81-8-19B	$Clayey_2$-$gravelly_{30}$-$silty_{31}$ $sand_{38}$	$Clayey_3$-$silty_{44}$ $sand_{54}$
Plug	40–45	81-8-19C	$Clayey_2$-$silty_{23}$-$gravelly_{32}$ $sand_{42}$	$Clayey_3$-$silty_{34}$ $sand_{62}$
Plug	40–45	81-8-19D	$Clayey_2$-$silty_{19}$-$gravelly_{30}$ $sand_{49}$	$Clayey_3$-$silty_{27}$ $sand_{70}$
Plug	40–45	81-8-19E	$Clayey_2$-$silty_{24}$ $gravel_{35}$ $sand_{38}$	$Clayey_3$-$silty_{37}$ $sand_{58}$
Plug		Missing		
Plug	ca. 30	81-8-19G	$Silty_4$ $sand_{47}$-$gravel_{48}$	$Silty_8$ $sand_{90}$
Plug	60–65	81-8-19H	$Clayey_1$-$gravelly_{17}$-$silty_{20}$ $sand_{62}$	$Clayey_1$-$silty_{24}$ $sand_{75}$
Plug	60–65	81-8-19I	Flocculated	
Plug	60–65	81-8-19J	$Clayey_2$-$gravelly_{14}$-$silty_{28}$ $sand_{56}$	$Clayey_2$-$silty_{32}$ $sand_{65}$

*Truncated data not available.
†Specimen locations are given in Figure 37.

TABLE 14. PE 83-3 (SPS. 83-9-8A–8F), GRAIN-SIZE ANALYSES, TRUNCATED AT 8 MM. PROMINENT BENCH INCLINED WESTERLY, ALTITUDE ABOUT 120 M, NEAR NORTHWEST END "AIRPORT RIDGE," RESOLUTE, CORNWALLIS ISLAND, N.W.T.

Location PE 83-3	Depth (cm)	Specimen	Specimen name	Matrix name	Weight (<8 mm) (g)	Total weight (g)
Plug, upslope side (of downslope plug with 15-cm rule, Fig. 39)	0–10	83-9-8A	Clayey$_6$-sandy$_{15}$-silty$_{33}$ gravel$_{47}$	Clayey$_{11}$-sandy$_{28}$ silt$_{61}$	569.2	836.2
Plug, downslope side (of downslope plug with 15-cm rule, Fig. 39)	0–10	83-9-8B	Muddy$_3$-sandy$_5$ gravel$_{92}$*	Muddy$_{42}$ sand$_{58}$*	328.4	824.4
Plug, downslope side (middle of downslope plug with 15-cm rule, Fig. 39)	20–30	83-9-8C	Clayey$_1$-silty$_4$-sandy$_7$ gravel$_{87}$	Clayey$_{10}$-silty$_{34}$ sand$_{56}$	198.6	863.4
Gravel adjacent to plugs	0–10	83-9-8D	Muddy$_4$-sandy$_5$ gravel$_{92}$*	Muddy$_{43}$ sand$_{57}$*	253.8	1,536.1
Gravel adjacent to plugs	10–20	83-9-8E	Clayey$_2$-silty$_4$-sandy$_4$ gravel$_{91}$	Clayey$_{22}$ silt$_{38}$-sand$_{40}$	190.9	1,244.6
Gravel adjacent to plugs	20–30	83-9-8F	Clayey$_1$-silty$_1$-sandy$_2$ gravel$_{97}$	Clayey$_{20}$-silty$_{28}$ sand$_{52}$	578.6	1,452.9

*Mud = silt + clay.

TABLE 15. PE 86-3 (SPS. 86-7-12A–12E), GRAIN-SIZE ANALYSES, TRUNCATED AT 8 MM. NORTH OF NORTH TRANSMITTER STATION AND SEVERAL METERS SOUTH OF MCMASTER RIVER BANK TOP, RESOLUTE, CORNWALLIS ISLAND, N.W.T.

Location PE 86-3	Depth (cm)	Specimen	Specimen name	Matrix name	Weight (<8 mm) (g)	Total weight (g)
Plug	0–10	86-7-12A	Clayey$_3$-gravelly$_{15}$-silty$_{32}$ sand$_{50}$	Clayey$_4$-silty$_{37}$ sand$_{59}$	609.7	901.5
Plug	10–20	86-7-12B	Clayey$_4$-gravelly$_{14}$ sand$_{40}$-silt$_{42}$	Clayey$_4$ sand$_{46}$-silt$_{49}$	510.0	1,274.7
Plug	20–30	86-7-12C	Clayey$_3$-gravelly$_{13}$ sand$_{41}$-silt$_{43}$	Clayey$_4$ sand$_{47}$-silt$_{49}$	781.1	1,739.9
Plug	30–40	86-7-12D	Clayey$_5$-gravelly$_{12}$ sand$_{40}$-silt$_{44}$	Clayey$_5$-sandy$_{45}$ silt$_{50}$	774.8	1,487.9
Plug	40–50	86-7-12E	Clayey$_7$-gravelly$_{15}$ silt$_{38}$-sand$_{40}$	Clayey$_9$ silt$_{45}$-sand$_{47}$	932.0	1,519.3

TABLE 16. S-CIRCLE EXCAVATION 88-A (SPS. 88-9-1A–1N), GRAIN-SIZE ANALYSES, TRUNCATED AT 8 MM. ALTITUDE ABOUT 83 M, SOME 100 M NORTH OF ROAD TOWARD TACAN BUILDING AND 100 M NORTH OF VOR ROAD, RESOLUTE, CORNWALLIS ISLAND, N.W.T.

Location S-Circle Excavation 88-A	Depth (cm)	Specimen	Specimen name	Matrix name	Weight (<8 mm) (g)	Total weight (g)
Northwest face, central sector	0–5	88-9-1A	$Clayey_{6}$-$silty_{24}$-$sandy_{31}$ $gravel_{36}$	$Clayey_{9}$-$silty_{40}$ $sand_{51}$	492.5	810.8
Northwest face, central sector	5–10	88-9-1B	$Clayey_{8}$-$gravelly_{23}$-$silty_{26}$ $sand_{43}$	$Clayey_{10}$-$silty_{34}$ $sand_{56}$	637.9	683.0
Northwest face, central sector	10–20	88-9-1C	$Clayey_{2}$-$silty_{18}$-$gravelly_{28}$ $sand_{51}$	$Clayey_{3}$-$silty_{25}$ $sand_{72}$	966.7	1,223.6
Northwest face, central sector	20–30	88-9-1D	$Clayey_{8}$-$silty_{13}$-$gravelly_{22}$ $sand_{58}$	$Clayey_{10}$-$silty_{17}$ $sand_{74}$	584.1	675.6
Northwest face, central sector	30–40	88-9-1E	$Clayey_{9}$-$silty_{17}$-$gravelly_{21}$ $sand_{53}$	$Clayey_{11}$-$silty_{22}$ $sand_{67}$	801.3	864.9
Northwest face, central sector	40–50	88-9-1F	$Clayey_{10}$-$silty_{15}$-$gravelly_{32}$ $sand_{43}$	$Clayey_{15}$-$silty_{22}$ $sand_{64}$	1,390.0	1,753.9
Northwest face, northeast sector	0–5	88-9-1G	$Clayey_{3}$-$silty_{24}$-$gravelly_{27}$ $sand_{46}$	$Clayey_{4}$-$silty_{33}$ $sand_{64}$	569.3	703.1
Northwest face, northeast sector	5–10	88-9-1H	$Clayey_{3}$-$silty_{21}$-$gravelly_{22}$ $sand_{54}$	$Clayey_{4}$-$silty_{27}$ $sand_{69}$	420.1	591.6
Northwest face, northeast sector	10–20	88-9-1I	$Clayey_{3}$-$silty_{17}$-$gravelly_{25}$ $sand_{54}$	$Clayey_{4}$-$silty_{23}$ $sand_{73}$	845.5	962.9
Northwest face, northeast sector	20–30	88-9-1J	$Clayey_{2}$-$silty_{17}$-$gravelly_{28}$ $sand_{53}$	$Clayey_{3}$-$silty_{23}$ $sand_{73}$	645.4	795.5
Northwest face, northeast sector	30–40	88-9-1K	$Clayey_{8}$-$silty_{17}$-$gravelly_{22}$ $sand_{53}$	$Clayey_{10}$-$silty_{22}$ $sand_{68}$	691.8	980.5
Northwest face, northeast sector	40–50	88-9-1L	$Clayey_{4}$-$silty_{21}$-$gravelly_{28}$ $sand_{48}$	$Clayey_{5}$-$silty_{29}$ $sand_{66}$	1,081.0	1,390.8
Southeast face, central sector	0–10	88-9-1M	$Gravelly_{19}$-$sandy_{38}$ mud_{43}*	$Sandy_{47}$ mud_{53}*	11.6	1,582.0
Southeast face, central sector	30–40	88-9-1N	$Muddy_{8}$-$sandy_{15}$ $gravel_{77}$*	$Muddy_{34}$ $sand_{66}$*	27.2	883.6

*Mud = silt + clay.

APPENDIX A, TABLE 1. CLIMATE SUMMARY, RESOLUTE A, CORNWALLIS ISLAND, N.W.T., 1947–1990. LATITUDE 74°43'N; LONGITUDE 94°59'W, ALTITUDE 67 M. MODIFIED FROM ENVIRONMENT CANADA, ATMOSPHERIC ENVIRONMENT SERVICE, 1993, *CANADIAN CLIMATE NORMALS/NORMALES CLIMATIQUES AU CANADA/1961–90*, EXCEPT AS OTHERWISE NOTED

	Jan	Feb	Mar	Apr	May	Jun	Jul	Aug	Sep	Oct	Nov	Dec	Year*
Temperature													
Daily maximum (°C)	-28.5	-29.4	-27.7	-19.9	-7.9	1.6	6.8	4.3	-2.8	-12.1	-20.9	-25.5	-13.5
Daily minimum (°C)	-35.8	-36.7	-34.9	-27.3	-14.3	-2.9	1.3	-0.5	-7.3	-18.5	-27.9	-32.7	-19.8
Daily mean (°C)†	-32.0	-33.0	-31.2	-23.5	-11.0	-0.6	4.0	1.9	-5.0	-15.2	-24.3	-29.0	-16.6
Extreme maximum (°C)	-0.8	-3.9	-2.7	0.0	4.8	13.9	18.3	15.0	9.4	0.7	-2.8	-4.3	
Date	1977/11	1963/04	1989/15	1975/29	1988/17	1951/30	1962/21	1949/06	1973/01	1984/13	1968/03	1983/24	
Extreme minimum (°C)	-52.2	-52.0	-51.7	-42.1	-29.4	-16.7	-3.1	9.0	-20.6	-37.3	-42.8	-46.1	
Date	1966/07	1979/14	1956/16	1983/05	1961/04	1974/05	1982/21	1985/27	1975/29	1986/23	1967/21	1948/27	
Degree days below 0 °C	996.5	933.9	971.4	708.7	345.5	50.5	0.2	11.4	156.6	475.3	732.3	902.7	6,285
Freeze-thaw cycles‡ (-2.2 to +1.1 °C)													
1961–1970	0	0	0	0	0.4	4.4	0.2	4.4	2.2	0	0	0	11.6
1971–1980	0	0	0	0	0.9	3.2	0.2	6.2	1.9	0	0	0	12.4
1981–1990	0	0	0	0	0.7	3.9	0.6	2.2	1.9	0	0	0	9.3
Precipitation													
Rainfall (mm)	0.0	0.0T§	0.0	0.0T	0.0T	4.7	18.3	21.5	5.4	0.4	0.0T	0.0	50.4
Snowfall (cm)	3.8	3.5	5.0	6.8	10.0	8.1	4.7	10.3	18.6	14.6	6.5	5.3	97.3
Precipitation (mm)	3.5	3.2	4.7	6.2	8.3	12.7	23.4	31.5	22.8	13.1	5.7	4.6	139.6
Extreme daily rainfall (mm)	0.0	0.0	0.0	0.0	0.5	18.0	20.6	25.1	15.6	12.2	0.0	0.0	
Date	1990/31	1990/28	1990/31	1990/10	1985/23	1951/14	1967/24	1960/12	1985/11	1984/13	1990/30	1990/31	
Extreme daily snowfall (cm)	3.8	3.8	5.7	6.9	8.6	10.8	9.4	10.4	13.2	10.2	6.0	5.6	
Date	1979/04	1971/23	1981/07	1961/29	1948/10	1990/09	1974/22	1981/18	1977/18	1947/12	1988/01	1978/22	
Extreme daily precipitation (mm)	3.3	3.8	4.5	6.9	8.6	19.6	20.6	25.1	18.2	12.2	4.6	4.1	
Date	1979/04	1971/23	1984/24	1961/29	1948/10	1951/14	1967/24	1960/12	1978/16	1984/13	1950/08	1963/14	
Month-end snow cover (cm)	25	26	29	30	30	4	0	1	10	20	21	24	

APPENDIX A, TABLE 1 (continued). CLIMATE SUMMARY, RESOLUTE A, CORNWALLIS ISLAND, N.W.T., 1947–1990.
LATITUDE 74°43'N; LONGITUDE 94°59'W, ALTITUDE 67 M. MODIFIED FROM ENVIRONMENT CANADA, ATMOSPHERIC ENVIRONMENT SERVICE, 1993, *CANADIAN CLIMATE NORMALS/NORMALES CLIMATIQUES AU CANADA/1961–90*, EXCEPT AS OTHERWISE NOTED

	Jan	Feb	Mar	Apr	May	Jun	Jul	Aug	Sep	Oct	Nov	Dec	Year*
Days with													
Maximum temperature >0 °C	0	0	0	0	1	21	31	28	6	<1	0	0	87
Measurable rainfall	0	0	0	0	<1	3	8	8	2	<1	0	0	21
Measurable snowfall	5	5	6	7	9	6	3	6	11	12	7	6	84
Measurable precipitation	5	5	6	7	9	8	9	13	12	11	7	6	98
Freezing precipitation	0	<1	0	<1	1	3	<1	2	5	1	0	0	15
Fog	3	4	5	3	4	9	12	13	7	5	2	2	68
Sunshine (hrs)	0	0	144.7	281.3	309.8	261.0	277.4	160.3	58.9	27.6	0	0	
Wind													
Speed (km/h)	21	21	20	20	21	21	20	21	24	23	22	21	21
Most frequent direction	NW	NW	NW	NW	NW	NW	NW	NW	N	N	NW	NW	NW
Maximum hourly speed (km/h)	106	111	97	116	100	89	85	96	105	102	142	108	
Direction	N	N	E	E	E	E	E	E	E	E	E	E	
Maximum gust speed (km/h)	138	135	108	138	119	109	108	120	107	124	158	132	
Direction	N	E	E	E	E	E	E	E	E	E	E	E	

*Because of rounding, averages in the Year column may not exactly agree with the average of the monthly data in the same row.
†Period of record for Means is 1961 through 1990; for Extremes, 1947 through 1990.
‡Freeze-thaw cycles for 1961 through 1970 from Maxwell (1980, v. 1, p. 148; his Table 2.7, p. 175); for 1971 through 1982 calculated from Environment Canada, Atmospheric Environment Service, Monthly Record Meteorological Observations in Northern Canada; for 1983 through 1990 from microfiche or copy of station worksheets.
§T = Trace.

APPENDIX B, TABLE 1. DAILY AVERAGE SOIL TEMPERATURES, RESOLUTE, CORNWALLIS ISLAND, N.W.T., 28 AUGUST–26 SEPTEMBER 1955 (READINGS EVERY 4 HOURS) FOR PERIOD OF FREEZE-BACK. EXTRACTED FROM COOK (1955, TABLE 3, p. 246; CF. COOK AND RAICHE, 1962, p. 67)

	Clay 15 m SE of shattered rock and gravel				Shattered rock and gravel. Alt. 12.5 m				Surface daily air, Stevenson Screen			
	20.3 cm (8 in.)		50.8 cm (20 in.)		20.3 cm (8 in.)		50.8 cm (20 in.)		Maximum		Minimum	
Date	°C	°F	°C	°F	°C	°F	°C	°F	°C	°F	°C	°F
28 Aug.	0.11	32.2	0.06	32.1	0.33	32.6	0.11	32.2	1.11	34.0	0.11	32.2
29	0.44	32.8	0.06	32.1	0.78	33.4	0.28	32.5	1.94	35.5	0.11	32.2
30	0.22	32.4	0.06	32.1	0.33	32.6	0.17	32.3	0.89	33.6	-1.00	30.2
31	-0.17	31.7	-0.06	31.9	-0.06	31.9	-0.11	31.8	-0.28	31.5	-1.72	28.9
1 Sept.	-0.28	31.5	-0.17	31.7	-0.06	31.9	-0.17	31.7	-0.33	31.4	-1.89	28.6
2	-0.33	31.4	-0.17	31.7	-0.28	31.5	-0.22	31.6	-0.17	31.7	-2.22	28.0
3	-0.33	31.4	-0.17	31.7	-0.06	31.9	-0.22	31.6	-0.67	30.8	-3.50	25.7
4	-0.33	31.4	-0.17	31.7	-0.06	31.9	-0.22	31.6	-1.89	28.6	-3.78	25.2
5	-0.33	31.4	-0.17	31.7	-0.17	31.7	-0.22	31.6	-2.00	28.4	-5.61	21.9
6	-0.33	31.4	-0.17	31.7	-0.11	31.8	-0.17	31.7	-1.61	29.1	-3.89	25.0
7	-0.39	31.3	-0.17	31.7	-0.11	31.8	-0.17	31.7	-1.06	30.1	-3.11	26.4
8	-0.39	31.3	-0.17	31.7	-0.22	31.6	-0.22	31.6	0.00	32.0	-4.06	24.7
9	-0.44	31.2	-0.22	31.6	-0.22	31.6	-0.22	31.6	-0.44	31.2	-3.89	25.0
10	-0.44	31.2	-0.22	31.6	-0.22	31.6	-0.22	31.6	-2.67	27.2	-7.83	17.9
11	-0.50	31.1	-0.22	31.6	-0.67	30.8	-0.22	31.6	-3.44	25.8	-6.67	20.0
12	-0.50	31.1	-0.22	31.6	-1.11	30.0	-0.22	31.6	-4.56	23.8	-6.67	20.0
13	-0.56	31.0	-0.22	31.6	-1.44	29.4	-0.28	31.5	-3.72	25.3	-6.89	19.6
14	-0.72	30.7	-0.22	31.6	-1.72	28.9	-0.44	31.2	-3.89	25.0	-9.61	14.7
15	-1.00	30.2	-0.22	31.6	-2.28	27.9	-0.83	30.5	-5.06	22.9	-11.50	11.3
16	-1.00	30.2	-0.22	31.6	-2.00	28.4	-1.28	29.7	-2.56	27.4	-7.00	19.4
17	-0.94	30.3	-0.22	31.6	-1.72	28.9	-1.67	29.0	-1.89	28.6	-5.50	22.1
18	-0.83	30.5	-0.28	31.5	-1.28	29.7	-1.78	28.8	-0.33	31.4	-2.50	27.5
19	-0.78	30.6	-0.28	31.5	-1.39	29.5	-1.89	28.6	-1.17	29.9	-4.56	23.8
20	-0.78	30.6	-0.28	31.5	-1.44	29.4	-2.00	28.4	-0.89	30.4	-5.56	22.0
21	-0.89	30.4	-0.33	31.4	-2.22	28.0	-2.28	27.9	-4.06	24.7	-8.39	16.9
22	-0.83	30.5	-0.39	31.3	-2.33	27.8	-2.56	27.4	-3.67	25.4	-5.22	22.6
23	-0.89	30.4	-0.39	31.3	-3.33	26.0	-2.83	26.9	-5.44	22.2	-9.94	14.1
24	-1.06	30.1	-0.44	31.2	-3.67	25.4	-3.33	26.0	-6.72	19.9	-10.00	14.0
25	-1.11	30.0	-0.56	31.0	-3.78	25.2	-3.50	25.7	-4.06	24.7	-6.78	19.8
26	-1.50	29.3	-0.67	30.8	-4.17	24.5	-3.72	25.3	-4.39	24.1	-7.67	18.2

APPENDIX B, TABLE 2. SOIL FREEZE-THAW CYCLES, RESOLUTE, CORNWALLIS ISLAND, N.W.T., 1 MAY– 30 SEPTEMBER 1960. MODIFIED FROM COOK AND RAICHE (1962, TABLE 1, p. 67)

Depth	Range			Ice days	Frost-free days	Frost-change days (one or more crossings of 0 °C)
	0 to -2.2 °C (32 to 28 °F)	1.1 to -2.2 °C (34 to 28 °F)	1.7 to -3.9 °C (35 to 25°F)			
Air (Stevenson screen)	15	9	3	57	59	37
Ground surface	23	18	7	43	66	44
2.5 cm shattered rock*	1	1	0	58	82	13
10 cm clay*	0	0	0	69	76	8
20 cm clay*	0	0	0	70	75	9

*The soil temperatures are from two different but nearby locations, one involving shattered rock at depth 2.5 cm, the other about 15 m distant being "... a pocket of clay at depths of 10 and 20 cm ... representative of the centres of ... sorted circles and polygons" (Cook and Raiche, 1962, p. 67). The central soil of sorted circles of the plug variety in some other Resolute areas is a fines-rich gravel.

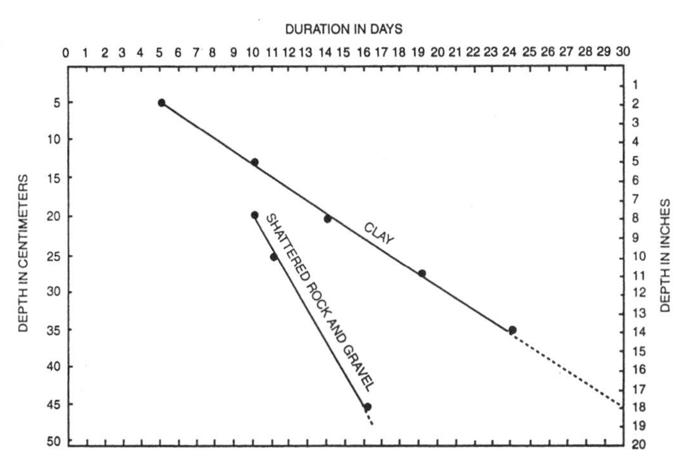

Figure 1. Duration of zero curtain in shattered rock and gravel, altitude 12.5 m, and in nearby clay, Resolute, Cornwallis Island, N.W.T., 1955. After Cook (1955, his Fig. 5, p. 245).

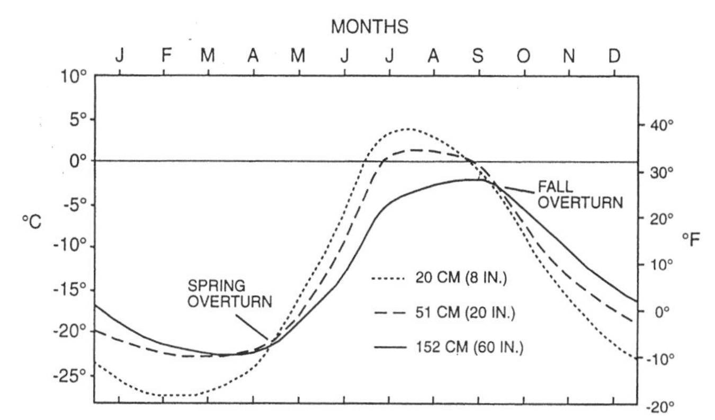

Figure 2. Spring and fall soil-temperature overturn in shattered rock and gravel at depths of 20, 51, and 152 cm (8, 20, and 60 in.), Resolute, Cornwallis Island, N.W.T., 1954. Modified from Cook (1955, his Fig. 4, p. 243).

APPENDIX C, TABLE 1. RADIOCARBON DATES OF SELECTED SPECIMENS FROM RESOLUTE AREA, CORNWALLIS ISLAND, N.W.T. UNIVERSITY OF WASHINGTON QUATERNARY ISOTOPE LABORATORY (QL SERIES)*

QL number	^{14}C age (yr BP)	Material†	Location	Altitude (m)
1904	9570 ± 40	Shells	Southwest slope, Prospect Hills	113 ± 2
4068	4950 ± 40	Shells *Mya truncata* (Sp. 85-8-9A)	ES C. PE 85-8-8, depth 50–70 cm	16 ± ½
4069	6180 ± 30	Shell fragments *Hiatella arctica, Mya truncata* (Sp. 85-8-8A1)	ES C. PE 85-8-8. Plug depth 0–50 cm	16 ± ½
4070	29,200 + 1,400 - 1,200	Shell fragments (Sp. 85-7-25C)	East-facing cut bank lower Mecham River, ca. 2 km east of Resolute Hamlet	24 ± 3
4071	8280 ± 40	Shells *Hiatella arctica, Mya truncata* (Sp. 85-7-25D)	Bench, west side lower Mecham River, ca. 2 km east of Resolute Hamlet	30 ± 3
4073	9790 ± 50	Shells *Hiatella arctica* (Linné), *Mya truncata* (Linné) Barnacles Balanus sp. (Sp. 85-7-21B)	Inner edge bench, south side gully immediately south of Char Lake	117 ± 3
4129	4470 ± 150	Seal fibula (Sp. 85-8-8A2)	ES C. PE 85-8-8. Border gravel, depth 10–20 cm	16 ± ½
4328	43,000 + 3,800 - 2,600	Dark, fine-grained organic streaks (Sp. 88-7-15A2)	East-facing cut bank lower Mecham River, ca. 10 m north of QL-4070	23 ± 3
4329	35,000 ± 1,800	Small, dark, fine-grained organic concentrations (plant impressions?) (Sp. 88-7-15A3)	East-facing cut bank lower Mecham River, ca. 10 m north of QL-4070	23 ± 3
4604	9140 ± 50	Shells (Sp. 90-4)	Plug in stony area, second swale east-southeast of TACAN Building	85 ± 1

*Courtesy, Professor Minze Stuiver, Director. An earlier series of Cornwallis Island dates appeared in Washburn and Stuiver (1985).
†Sp. (specimen) numbers are those of the author (ALW).

ENDNOTES

1. Kaujuitok (the place where the sun never rises) is the Inuktituk name for Resolute Bay.

[2.] Where measurements are given in both English and metric units, the measurements in English units are taken from the work being cited, and the measurements in metric units are my conversion.

[3.] Cook's temperature installation was in shattered rock and gravel on a prominent "raised beach line" (Cook, 1955, p. 238) as were many of the plugs and plug circles that I excavated in beach gravel. However, the plug soil consisted of fines-rich gravel instead of clay. Some areal variability is to be expected, and Cook's photograph (1955, p. 247, his Fig. 6) clearly shows ice-lensed fine soil.

4. The term dolomitic where used in the following is not intended to imply any particular ratio of dolomite to limestone, only that a rock will effervesce slightly with 10% HCl if scratched but not otherwise.

5. I have not been able to confirm the observation that any mounds (plug circles) rest on a thin soil. Perhaps the reference is to roundstones, which in places would be derived from circle soil that had moved slightly downslope over immediately adjacent weathered gravel.

6. Grain-size limits of fines were not cited. Cook's (1956, p. 14) text reference to 43.5% fines by weight in his Table V is probably in error and actually refers to stones, judging from the internal consistency of his Tables IV and V (p. 14–15). See Note 12.

7. The hill is the site of an unusual assemblage of circular to elongate depressions, some at least 65 cm deep and up to 2 m in diameter where circular. They are probably thermokarst features consequent on thawing of ice concentrations.

8. The term stone pit was applied by G. Lundqvist (1949, p. 336) to forms surrounded by vegetation. However, a variety of stony pits has been described in the geocryologic literature, and a variety of explanations offered (cf. Washburn, 1979, p. 131–132, 169). Such features are not well known and are probably of disparate origins.

9. However, Huxley and Odell (1924, p. 211–212) noted that convexities as well as depressions could occur in the frost table (tjaele) at shallow depths.

10. Palm and Tweitereid (1977, p. 146), citing Bénard's results as being due really to a temperature-induced surface-tension gradient, noted that the comparison with temperature-induced buoyancy forces was poorly founded (cf. Hallet, 1987, p. 545–546).

11. The term soil circulation is used here in place of soil convection, which although common in the literature has been criticized as implying an instability controlled directly by water temperature rather than by volume of water (cf. Bertouille, 1978, p. 29, 31; Van Vliet-Lanoë, 1988a, p. 477). Soil circulation as the preferred term has also been adopted by Hallet and Waddington (1991, p. 253). By it they specified ". . . the circulatory or churning pattern of soil motion (its kinematics). The pattern combines a general ascent of fine-grained soil in the center of sorted circles, a descent of soil at the periphery of fine-grained soil domains, and appropriate soil recirculation at depths to sustain the observed near-surface soil motion. It does not imply (1) that the soil is fluidized, (2) that motion is driven by buoyancy, or (3) that the subsurface motion is closely approximated by circular particle trajectories characteristic of Bénard convection cells, as was proposed (e.g. Hallet and Prestrud, 1986) and subsequently questioned (Pissart, 1990 [p. 128])."

12. Despite the importance of relative soil densities, hard field data for the region of concern are in short supply. Data for Resolute plugs were presented by Cook (1956, his Tables IV–V). (Cook's statement [p. 14] that "Table V shows that the average weight of fine material in the plug was 43.5 percent of the total weight . . . " is apparently in error and refers to the stones column where this percentage appears. This interpretation is supported by the weight relations in Table V's being consistent with their volume relations in Table IV.) Plugs 1 through 6 (p. 14–15; cf. his Fig. 3) give an average bulk density of 1.36, with individual plug densities ranging from 0.87 to 1.71. The lowest value seems so low as to be suspect, and if plug 5 (the associated plug) is disregarded, the average becomes 1.49 and the spread 1.19 to 1.71. The bordering gravel was not analyzed. The bulk density of two Resolute plugs (collected by me and determined at the Department of Geography, University of British Columbia, courtesy Professor M. A. Church) were very similar to each other (Table 4): 2.07 (PE 90-1, Sp. 90-8-24) and 1.99 (PE 90-2, Sp. 90-9-3A). These values are appreciably higher than the Resolute values given by Cook as cited above and the value of 1.61 for an otherwise apparently similar plug from neighboring Devon Island (Table 1) (Bunting and Jackson, 1970, their Table 3, sps. 7–11, p. 203; cf. their Fig. 2, p. 195, and their Fig. 6, p. 201). The bulk density of the largely openwork gravel bordering the plug was 1.84 (Bunting and Jackson's specimens 1 through 4. Their specimens 5 and 6 are omitted here as being of problematic allocation as between plug and bordering gravel). No data were given for the gravel at the plug top. Thus, although the data are very meager, the gravel bordering this plug had a higher bulk density than the plug. Field data on bulk densities of plugs and bordering soils are much to be desired, and information on transient unstable density gradients would be of special interest but, as emphasized by Hallet and Waddington (1991, p. 275), evidence from presently fossil profiles would be unreliable.

13. The significance of cryostatic pressure in a more general context is supported by Vandenberghe (1988, p. 188, 193; 1992, p. 344–345). As he noted (1988, p. 190), the entire subject is complicated by "an emerging complexity in the study of active layer processes"—a complication that arises not only from its inherent complexity and the need for more data (as brought out by French's [1988] helpful review of such processes) but also by a sometimes overlapping, imprecise, and therefore confusing terminology. In any event, more observations are needed to prove or disprove the possible importance of cryostatic pressure.

[14.] This aspect is discussed later in the present report in the section "Differential frost heaving and surfaceward seepage."

15. This term is an extension of the sedimentary term "loadcasting (a) The formation or development of a load cast or load casts . . . " (AGI/G, p. 386), referring to a load cast as "A *sole mark*, usually measuring less than a meter in any direction, consisting of a swelling in the shape of a slight bulge, a deep or shallow rounded sack, a knobby excrescence, a highly irregular protrusion of sand or other coarse clastics extending downward into finer-grained, softer, and originally hydroplastic underlying material . . . " (AGI/G, p. 386).

[16.] I have not observed instances of expulsion of frost-shattered bedrock initiated along contraction cracks in soil to form RB S-circles or polygons, as diagrammed by Van Vliet-Lanoë (1988b, her Figs. 9, 11, p. 91, 94; 1988c, her Fig. 9, p. 1013), but I have seen occurrences in which the bedrock fragments reflected an underlying joint pattern in the bedrock itself (cf. Washburn, 1950, p. 49; Pl. 14, p. 52).

REFERENCES CITED

AGI/G American Geological Institute/Glossary. *See* Bates and Jackson, 1987.

Anderson, S. P., 1988, The upfreezing process: Experiments with a single clast: Geological Society of America Bulletin, v. 100, p. 609–621.

Anketell, J. M., Cegła, J., and Dżułyński, S., 1970, On the deformational structures in systems with reversed density gradients: Annales Société Géologique de Pologne (Rocznik Polskiego Towarzystwa Geologicznego), v. 40, p. 3–30.

Ballantyne, C. K., and Matthews, J. A., 1982, The development of sorted circles on recently deglaciated terrain, Jotunheimen, Norway: Arctic and Alpine Research, v. 14, p. 341–354.

Bates, R. L., and Jackson, J. A., eds., 1987, Glossary of geology (third edition): Alexandria, Virginia, American Geological Institute, 788 p.

Bénard, H., 1900, Les tourbillons cellulaires dans une nappe liquide: Revue des Sciences Pures et Appliqués, v. 11, p. 1261–1271, 1309–1328.

Benedict, J. B., 1978, Excavations at the Hungry Whistler Site, *in* Benedict, J. B., and Olson, B. L., 1978, The Mount Albion Complex—A study of prehistoric man and the altithermal: Center for Mountain Archeology (Ward, Colorado) Research Report 1, p. 1–75.

Benedict, J. B., 1992, Field and laboratory studies of patterned ground in a Colorado alpine region: University of Colorado, Institute of Arctic and Alpine Research Occasional Paper 49, 38 p.

Bertouille, H., 1976, Migration des pierres sous l'effet du gel et du dégel: Revue de Géomorphologie Dynamique, v. 25, p. 139–147.

Bertouille, H., 1978, Phénomènes de plasticité liés au gel: Cahier Géographique de Besançon, v. 17, p. 9–49.

Bibus, E., 1976, Geomorphologische Untersuchungen zur Hang- und Talentwicklung im zentralen West-Spitzbergen: Polarforschung, v. 45, p. 102–119.

Bird, J. B., 1967, The physiography of Arctic Canada: Baltimore, Maryland,

The Johns Hopkins University Press, 336 p.

Blake, W., Jr., 1970, Studies of glacial history in Arctic Canada. I: Pumice, radiocarbon dates, and differential postglacial uplift in the eastern Queen Elizabeth Islands: Canadian Journal of Earth Sciences, v. 7, p. 634–664.

Brewer, R., and Haldane, A. D., 1957, Preliminary experiments in the development of clay orientation in soils: Soil Science, v. 84, p. 301–309.

Brown, J.-L., and Gangloff, P., 1980, Géliformes et sols cryiques dans le sud de l'Abitibi, Québec: Géographie Physique et Quaternaire, v. 34, p. 137–158.

Büdel, J., 1960, Die Frostschutt-Zone Südost-Spitzbergens: Universität Bonn, Geographisches Institut, Colloquium Geographicum, v. 6, 105 p.

Büdel, J., 1961, Die Abtragungs-Vorgänge auf Spitzbergen im Umkreis der Barents-Insel (auf Grund der Stauferland-Expedition 1959/60): Deutscher Geographentag Köln (22–26 Mai 1961), Tagungsbericht und wissenschaftliche Abhandlungen, v. 33, p. 337–375.

Büdel, J., 1977, Klima-Geomorphologie: Berlin, Gebrüder Borntraeger, 304 p.

Büdel, J., 1982, Climatic geomorphology: Princeton, New Jersey, Princeton University Press, 443 p. (Translation of Büdel, 1977, by L. Fischer and D. Busche.)

Büdel, J., 1987, Die Abtragungsvorgänge in der exzessiven Talbildungszone Südost-Spitsbergens: Ergebnisse der Stauferland-Expedition, Heft 1: Stuttgart, Franz Steiner Verlag Wiesbaden GMBH, 131 p.

Bunting, B. T., and Jackson, R. H., 1970, Studies of patterned ground on SW Devon Island, N.W.T.: Geografiska Annaler, v. 52A, p. 194–208.

Burn, C. R., and Smith, M. W., 1993, Issues in Canadian permafrost research: Progress in Physical Geography, v. 17, p. 156–172.

Butrym, J., Cegła, J., Dżułyński, S., and Nakonieczny, S., 1964, New interpretation of periglacial structures: Polska Akademia Nauk, Oddzial W Krakowie, Folia Quaternia 17, 34 p.

Canada Soil Survey Committee, Subcommittee on Soil Classification, 1978, The Canadian system of soil classification: Ottawa, Supply and Services Canada, Canada Department of Agriculture Publication 1646, 164 p.

Casagrande, A., 1931, Discussion, *in* Benkelman, A. C., and Olmstead, F. R., A new theory of frost heaving: Proceedings, National Research Council Highway Research Board Annual Meeting, 11th, Volume 1: Washington, D.C., National Academy of Sciences–National Research Council, p. 169.

Cegła, J., 1973, Próba wyjaśnienia genezy gruntów strukturalnych SW Spitsbergenu w świetle teorii układów niestatecznego warstwowania gęstościowego (Tentative explanation of origin of structural grounds in SW Spitsbergen in the light of the hypothesis of systems with reversed density gradient): Czasopismo Geograficze, v. 44, p. 237–243.

Chambers, M. J. G., 1967, Investigations of patterned ground at Signy Island, South Orkney Islands. III: Miniature patterns, frost heaving and general conclusions: British Antarctic Survey Bulletin 12, p. 1–22.

Cheng, G., 1982, The forming process of thick layered ground ice: Scientia Sinica, ser. B, v. 25, p. 777–788.

Conrad, V., 1946, Polygon nets and their physical development: American Journal of Science, v. 244, p. 277–296.

Cook, F. A., 1955, Near surface soil temperature measurement at Resolute Bay, Northwest Territories: Arctic, v. 8, p. 237–249.

Cook, F. A., 1956, Additional notes on mud circles at Resolute Bay, Northwest Territories: Canadian Geographer, no. 8, p. 9–17.

Cook, F. A., 1958, Sorted circles at Resolute, N.W.T.: Geographical Bulletin, no. 11, p. 78–81.

Cook, F. A., 1959, Some types of patterned ground in Canada: Geographical Bulletin, no. 13, p. 73–81.

Cook, F. A., and Raiche, V. G., 1962, Freeze-thaw cycles at Resolute, N.W.T.: Geographical Bulletin, no. 18, p. 64–78.

Corte, A. E., 1961, The frost behavior of soils: Laboratory and field data for a new concept. Part 1: Vertical sorting: U.S. Army Cold Regions Research and Engineering Laboratory Research Report 85, Part 1, 22 p.

Corte, A. E., 1962a, The frost behavior of soils: Laboratory and field data for a new concept. Part 2: Horizontal sorting: U.S. Army Cold Regions Research and Engineering Laboratory Research Report 85, Part 2, 20 p.

Corte, A. E., 1962b, Relationship between four ground patterns, structure of the active layer, and type and distribution of ice in the permafrost: U.S. Army Cold Regions Research and Engineering Laboratory Research Report 88, 79 p. + appendices.

Corte, A. E., 1963, Relationship between four ground patterns, structure of the active layer, and type and distribution of ice in the permafrost: Biuletyn Peryglacjalny, v. 12, p. 7–90.

Corte, A. E., 1966, Particle sorting by repeated freezing and thawing: Biuletyn Peryglacjalny, v. 15, p. 175–240.

Corte, A. E., 1972, Laboratory formation of extrusion features by multicyclic freeze-thaw in soils: Centre de Géomorphologie de Caen Bulletin 13-14-15, p. 158–182.

Crampton, C. B., 1977, A study of the dynamics of hummocky microrelief in the Canadian north: Canadian Journal of Earth Sciences, v. 14, p. 639–649.

Cruickshank, J. G., 1971, Soils and terrain units around Resolute, Cornwallis Island: Arctic, v. 24, p. 195–209.

Dixon, J. C., 1986, Solute movement on hillslopes in the alpine environment of the Colorado Front Range, *in* Abrahams, A. D., ed., Hillslope processes: Boston, Allen & Unwin, p. 139–159.

Dredge, L. A., 1992, Breakup of limestone bedrock by frost shattering and chemical weathering, eastern Canadian Arctic: Arctic and Alpine Research, v. 24, p. 314–323.

Dyke, A. S., 1993, Glacial and sea level history of Lowther and Griffith Islands, Northwest Territories: A hint of tectonics: Géographie Physique et Quaternaire, v. 47, p. 133–145.

Dyke, A. S., and Prest, V. K., 1987, Late Wisconsinan and Holocene history of the Laurentide Ice Sheet: Géographie Physique et Quaternaire, v. 41, p. 237–263.

Dyke, A. S., and Zoltai, S. C., 1980, Radiocarbon-dated mudboils, central Canadian Arctic: Geological Survey of Canada Paper 80-1B, p. 271–275.

Dyke, A. S., Morris, T. F., and Green, D. E. C., 1991, Postglacial tectonic and sea level history of the central Canadian Arctic: Geological Survey of Canada Bulletin 397, 56 p.

Dyke, A. S., Morris, T. F., Green, D. E. C., and England, J., 1992, Quaternary geology of Prince of Wales Island, Arctic Canada: Geological Survey of Canada Memoir 433, 142 p.

Dyke, L., and Egginton, P., 1988, Till behavior and its relationship to active-layer hydrology, District of Keewatin, Northwest Territories: Canadian Geotechnical Journal, v. 25, p. 167–172.

Dyke, L., and Egginton, P., 1990, Influence of ice lens fabric on the hydraulic conductivity of thawing soil, *in* Pergélisol-Canada, Actes de la cinquième conférence Canadienne sur le pergélisol/Permafrost-Canada, Proceedings, Canadian Permafrost Conference, 5th, Québec City: Université Laval, Centre d'études nordiques, Collection Nordicana 54, p. 137–141.

Dżułyński, S., 1963, Polygonal structures in experiments and their bearing upon some periglacial phenomena: Académie Polonaise des Sciences, Bulletin, Série Sciences Géologiques et Géographiques, v. 11, p. 145–150.

Dżułyński, S., 1966, O strukturach sedymentacyjnych związnych z niestatecznym uwarstwieniem gęstościowym (Sedimentary structures resulting from convection-like pattern of motion): Annales de la Société Géologique de Pologne (Rocznik Polskiego Towarzstwa Geologicznego), v. 36, p. 3–21.

Edlund, S. A., 1991, Preliminary surficial geology of Cornwallis and adjacent islands, Northwest Territories: Geological Survey of Canada Paper 89–12, 30 p.

Edlund, S. A., 1992, Vegetation of Cornwallis Island and adjacent islands, Northwest Territories: Relationships between vegetation and surficial materials: Geological Survey of Canada Paper 89-26, 24 p. and Map 1767A.

Egginton, P. A., 1972, Observations on patterned ground phenomena found on Cornwallis Island, N.W.T. [B.A. Honours Thesis]: Hamilton, Ontario, McMaster University, Department of Geography, 157 p.

Egginton, P. A., 1979, Mudboil activity, central District of Keewatin: Geological Survey of Canada Paper 79-1B, p. 349–356.

Egginton, P. A., 1981, The impact of disturbance on mudboil activity, North Henrik Lake, District of Keewatin: Geological Survey of Canada Paper 81-1A, p. 299–303.

Egginton, P. A., and Dyke, L. D., 1982, Density gradients and injection structures in mudboils in central District of Keewatin: Geological Survey of Canada Paper 82-1B, p. 173–176.

Egginton, P. A., and Dyke, L. D., 1990, Apparent hydraulic conductivities associated with thawing, frost-susceptible soils: Permafrost and Periglacial Processes, v. 1, p. 69–77.

Egginton, P. A., and French, H. M., 1985, Solifluction and related processes, eastern Banks Island, N.W.T.: Canadian Journal of Earth Sciences, v. 22, p. 1671–1678.

Egginton, P. A., and Shilts, W. W., 1978, Rates of movement associated with mud boils, central District of Keewatin: Geological Survey of Canada Paper 78-1B, p. 203–206.

Eichler, H., 1981, Gesteinstemperaturen und Insolationsverwitterung im hocharktischen Bereich, Oobloyah Bay, N-Ellesmere Island, N.W.T., Kanada (Rock temperatures and insolation weathering in the High Arctic, Oobloyah Bay, Northern Ellesmere Island, N.W.T., Canada), *in* Barsch, D., and King, L., eds., Ergebnisse der Heidelberg Ellesmere Island Expedition: Heidelberger Geographische Arbeiten, v. 69, p. 441–464.

Elton, C. S., 1927, The nature and origin of soil-polygons in Spitsbergen: Geological Society of London Quarterly Journal, v. 83, p. 163–194.

Energy Mines and Resources Canada, 1985, District of Franklin, Northwest Territories, 1:50,000 [Map Series], Becher Bay (F8/F13). Extract, modified.

Environment Canada, 1993, Canadian climate normals—Normales climatiques au Canada/1961–1990, Yukon and Northwest Territories—Territoires du Yukon et du Nord-ouest: Ottawa, Environment Canada, Atmospheric Environment Service, 58 p.

Ershov, E. D., 1979, Vlagoperenos i kriogenneye tekstury v dispersnykh porodakh (Moisture transfer and cryogenic textures in fine-grained soils): Moscow, Izdatel'stvo Moskovskogo Universiteta, 214 p.

Ershov, E. D., Cheverev, V. G., Lebedenko, Yu. P., and Shevchenko, L. V., 1980, Water migration, formation of texture and ice segregation in freezing and thawing clayey soils, *in* English translations of the forty-nine Soviet papers, the one French paper, and the three invited Soviet theme papers, Part 1, International Conference on Permafrost, 3rd, Edmonton, 1978: Ottawa, National Research Council of Canada, NRCC 18119, p. 159–175.

Etzelmüller, B., and Sollid, J. L., 1991, The role of weathering and pedological processes for development of sorted circles on Kvadehuksletta, Svalbard—a short report: Polar Research, v. 9, p. 181–191.

Everett, K. R., 1968, Soil development in the Mould Bay and Isachsen areas, Queen Elizabeth Islands, Northwest Territories, Canada: Ohio State University Institute of Polar Studies Report 24, 75 p.

Fahey, B. D., 1975, Nonsorted circle development in a Colorado alpine location: Geografiska Annaler, v. 57A, p. 153–164.

Flint, R. F., Sanders, J. E., and Rodgers, J., 1960a, Synmictite: A name for nonsorted terrigeneous sedimentary rocks that contain a wide range of particle sizes: Geological Society of America Bulletin, v. 71, p. 507–510.

Flint, R. F., Sanders, J. E., and Rodgers, J., 1960b, Diamictite, a substitute term for synmictite: Geological Society of America Bulletin, v. 71, p. 1809.

Forman, S. L., and Miller, G. H., 1984, Time-dependent soil morphologies and pedogenic processes on raised beaches, Bröggerhalvöya, Spitsbergen, Svalbard Archipelago: Arctic and Alpine Research, v. 16, p. 381–394.

French, H. M., 1988, Active layer processes, *in* Clark, H. M., ed., Advances in periglacial geomorphology: New York, John Wiley & Sons, p. 151–159.

Frödin, J., 1918, Über das Verhältnis zwischen Vegetation und Erdfliessen in den alpinen Regionen des schwedischen Lappland: Lunds Universitet, Årsskrift, N.F., Avd. 2, v. 14, 32 p.

Gleason, K. J., Krantz, W. B., and Caine, N., 1988, Parametric effects in the filtration free convection model for patterned ground, *in* Senneset, K., ed., Proceedings, Permafrost International Conference, 5th, Trondheim, Norway, Volume 1: Trondheim, Norway, Tapir Publishers, p. 349–354.

Goldthwait, R. P., 1976, Frost sorted patterned ground: A review: Quaternary Research, v. 6, p. 27–35.

Graf, K. J., 1971, Beiträge zur Solifluction in den Bündner Alpen (Schweiz) und in den Anden Perus und Boliviens [Ph.D. inaugural dissertation]: Zürich, University of Zürich, Juris Druck, 152 p.

Gripp, K., 1926, Über Frost und Strukturboden auf Spitzbergen: Gesellschaft für Edkunde zu Berlin, Zeitschrift, p. 351–354.

Gripp, K., 1927, Beiträge zur Geologie von Spitzbergen: Naturwissenschaftlicher Verein Hamburg, Abhandlungen, v. 21, p. 1–38.

Gripp, K., 1929, Glaciologische und geologische Ergebnisse der Hamburgischen Spitzbergen-Expedition 1927: Naturwissenschaftlicher Verein Hamburg, Abhandlungen, v. 22, p. 145–249.

Gripp, K., 1952, Zwei Beiträge zur Frage der periglazialen Vorgänge: Geologische Institut der Universität Kiel, Meyniana, v. 1, p. 112–118.

Gripp, K., and Simon, W. G., 1933, Experimente zum Brodelbodenproblem: Centralblatt für Mineralogie, v. 1933, Abt. B, p. 433–440.

Gripp, K., and Simon, W. G., 1934a, Die experimentelle Darstellung des Brodelbodens: Die Naturwissenschaften, v. 22, p. 8–10.

Gripp, K., and Simon, W. G., 1934b, Nochmals zum Problem des Brodelbodens: Centralblatt für Mineralogie, v. 1934, Abt. B, p. 283–286.

Hall, K., 1991, The allocation of freeze-thaw weathering mechanisms in geophysical studies: A critical comment: South African Geographical Journal, v. 73, p. 10–13.

Hall, K., and Hall, A., 1991, Thermal gradients and rock weathering at low temperatures: Some simulation data: Permafrost and Periglacial Processes, v. 2, p. 103–112.

Hallet, B., 1987, On geomorphic patterns with a focus on stone circles viewed as a free-convection phenomenon, *in* Nicolis, C., and Nicolis, G., eds., Irreversible phenomena and dynamical systems analysis in geosciences: Dordrecht, D. Reidel Publishing, p. 533–553.

Hallet, B., 1990, Self-organization in freezing soils: From microscopic ice lenses to patterned ground: Canadian Journal of Physics, v. 68, p. 842–852.

Hallet, B., 1993, Geometry and size of sorted patterns in periglacial soils reflect convection; but what is convecting? [abs.]: Eos (Transactions, American Geophysical Union), Supplement, 20 April, p. 152.

Hallet, B., and Prestrud, S., 1986, Dynamics of periglacial sorted circles in western Spitsbergen: Quaternary Research, v. 26, p. 81–99.

Hallet, B., and Waddington, E. D., 1991, Buoyancy forces induced by freeze-thaw in the active layer: Implications for diapirism and soil circulation, *in* Dixon, J. C., and Abrahams, A. D., eds., Periglacial geomorphology. London, John Wiley and Sons Ltd., p. 251–279.

Hallet, B., Anderson, S. P., Stubbs, C. W., and Gregory, E. C., 1988, Surface soil displacements in sorted circles, western Spitsbergen, *in* Senneset, K., ed., Proceedings, Permafrost International Conference, 5th, Trondheim, Norway, Volume 1: Trondheim, Norway, Tapir Publishers, p. 770–775

Hallet, B., Walder, J. S., and Stubbs, C. W., 1991, Weathering by segregation ice growth in microcracks at sustained sub-zero temperatures: Verification from an experimental study using accoustic emissions: Permafrost and Periglacial Processes, v. 3, p. 283–300.

Hamberg, A., 1915, Zur Kenntnis der Vorgänge im Erdboden beim Gefrieren und Auftauen sowie Bemerkungen über die erste Kristillisation des Eises in Wasser: Geologiska Föreningen Stockholm Förhandlingar, v. 37, p. 583–619.

Harris, C., 1990, Micromorphology and microfabrics of sorted circles, Front Range, Colorado, U.S.A., *in* Pergélisol-Canada, Actes de la cinquième conférence Canadienne sur le pergélisol/Permafrost-Canada, Proceedings, Canadian Permafrost Conference, 5th, Québec City: Université Laval, Centre d'études nordiques, Collection Nordicana 54, p. 89–94.

Harris, C., and Cook, J. D., 1988, Micromorphology and microfabrics of sorted circles, Jotunheimen, southern Norway, *in* Senneset, K., ed., Proceedings, Permafrost International Conference, 5th, Trondheim, Norway, Volume 1: Trondheim, Norway, Tapir Publishers, p. 776–783.

Harris, S. A., 1986, The permafrost environment: London, Croom Helm, 276 p.

Harris, S. A., 1988, Observations on the redistribution of moisture in the active layer and permafrost, *in* Senneset, K., ed., Proceedings, Permafrost International Conference, 5th, Trondheim, Norway, Volume 1: Trondheim, Norway, Tapir Publishers, p. 364–369.

Herz, K., and Andreas, G., 1966, Untersuchungen zur Morphologie der periglazialen Auftauschicht im Kongsfjordgebiet (Westspitzbergen): Petermanns Geographische Mitteilungen, v. 110, p. 190–198.

Högbom, B., 1914, Über die geologische Bedeutung des Frostes: Universitetet Uppsala, Geologiska Institutet, Bulletin, v. 12 (1913–1914), p. 257–389.

Hopkins, D. M., and Sigafoos, R. S., 1951, Frost action and vegetation patterns on Seward Peninsula, Alaska: U.S. Geological Survey Bulletin 974-C, p. 51–101.

Huxley, J. S., and Odell, N. E., 1924, Notes on surface markings in Spitsbergen: Geographical Journal, v. 63, p. 207–229.

Imeson, A. C., Vis, M., and Duysings, J.J.H.M., 1984, Surface and subsurface sources of suspended solids in forested drainage basins in the Keuper region of Luxembourg, *in* Burt, T. P., and Walling, D. E., eds., Catchment experiments in fluvial geomorphology, Proceedings, International Geographical Union, Commission on Field Experiments Meeting, Exeter and Huddersfield, U.K., 1981: Norwich, England, Geobooks, p. 219–233.

Jahn, A., 1946, O niektórych formach gleb strukturalnych Grenlandii Zachodniej (About some forms of structural soil markings in West Greenland): Przeglad Geograficzny, v. 20, p. 73–89.

Jahn, A., 1948, Badania nad strukturą i temperaturą gleb w Grenlandi zachodniej (Research on the structure and temperature of the soils in western Greenland): Bulletin International de l'Académie Polonaise des Sciences et des Lettres, Classe des Sciences Mathématiques et Naturelles, Série A—Sciences Mathématiques, No. Sommaire A 1940–1946, p. 50–59.

Jahn, A., 1963, Origin and development of patterned ground in Spitsbergen, *in* Proceedings, Permafrost International Conference [1st], Lafayette, Indiana: Washington, D.C., National Academy of Sciences, National Research Council Publication 1287, p. 140–145.

Jania, J., 1977, Debris forms on the Skoddefjellet slope, *in* Results of investigations of the Polish Scientific Spitsbergen expeditions 1970–1974, Volume 2: Acta Universitatis Wratislaviensis, no. 387, p. 91–117.

Johansson, S., 1914, Die Festigkeit der Bodenarten bei verschiedenem Wassergehalt nebst Vorschlag zu einer Klassifikation: Sveriges Geologiska Undersökning, Avhandlingar och Uppsatser, Årsbok 7 (1913), no. 3 (ser. C, no. 256), 110 p.

Kersten, M. S., 1949, Laboratory research for the determination of the thermal properties of soils: Final report to U.S. Army Corps of Engineers, St. Paul District: St. Paul, University of Minnesota Engineering Experiment Station, 227 p.

King, C. A. M., and Buckley, J. T., 1969, Geomorphological investigations in west-central Baffin Island, N.W.T., Canada: Arctic and Alpine Research, v. 1, p. 105–120.

Kling, J., 1996, Relict patterned ground in Rostu, northernmost Sweden: Geografiska Annaler, v. 78A, p. 61–72.

Krantz, W. B., 1990, Self-organization manifest as patterned ground in recurrently frozen soils: Earth Science Reviews, v. 29, p. 117–130.

Krantz, W. B., Gleason, K. J., and Caine, N., 1988, Patterned ground: Scientific American, v. 259, p. 68–76.

Kreida, N. A., 1959, Soils of the eastern European tundras: Soviet Soil Science, no. 1, p. 51–56. (Translated from Pochvovedenie, 1958, no. 1, p. 62–67.)

Lagov, P. A., and Parmuzina, O. Yu., 1978, K voprosy o l'dovydelenii v sezonnotalom sloe (Ice formation in the seasonally thawing layer), *in* Melnikov, P. I., and Tolstikhin, N. I., series eds., Obshchee Merzlotovedenie (series): Novosibirsk, USSR, Nauka, p. 56–59.

Lewkowicz, A. G., and French, H. M., 1982, The hydrology of small runoff plots in an area of continuous permafrost, Banks Island, N.W.T., *in* French, H. M., ed., The Roger J. E. Brown Memorial Volume: Proceedings, Canadian Permafrost Conference, 4th, Calgary, 1981: Ottawa, National Research Council of Canada, p. 151–162.

Locke, W. W., 1986, Fine particle translocation in soils developed on glacial deposits, southern Baffin Island, N.W.T., Canada: Arctic and Alpine Research, v. 18, p. 33–43.

Low, A. R., 1925, The instability of viscous fluid motion: Nature, v. 115, p. 299–300.

Lundqvist, G., 1949, The orientation of the block material in certain species of flow earth: Geografiska Annaler, häfte 1-2, p. 335–347.

Lundqvist, J., 1962, Patterned ground and related frost phenomena in Sweden: Sveriges Geologiska Undersökning, Avhandlingar och Uppsatser, Årsbok 55 (1961), no. 7 (ser. C, no. 583), 101 p.

Mackay, J. R., 1953, Fissures and mud circles on Cornwallis Island, N.W.T.: Canadian Geographer, no. 3, p. 31–37.

Mackay, J. R., 1972, The world of underground ice: Association of American Geographers Annals, v. 62, p. 1–22.

Mackay, J. R., 1979, An equilibrium model for hummocks (nonsorted circles), Garry Island, Northwest Territories: Geological Survey of Canada Paper 79-1A, p. 165–167.

Mackay, J. R., 1980, The origin of hummocks, western Arctic coast, Canada: Canadian Journal of Earth Sciences, v. 17, p. 996–1006.

Mackay, J. R., 1981, Active layer slope movement in a continuous permafrost environment, Garry Island, Northwest Territories, Canada: Canadian Journal of Earth Sciences, v. 18, p. 1666–1680.

Mackay, J. R., 1983, Downward water movement into frozen ground, western arctic coast, Canada: Canadian Journal of Earth Sciences, v. 20, p. 120–134.

Mackay, J. R., and MacKay, D. K., 1975, Cryostatic pressures in nonsorted circles (mud hummocks), Inuvik, Northwest Territories: Canadian Journal of Earth Sciences, v. 13, p. 889–897.

Mann, D. H., Sletten, R. S., and Ugolini, F. C., 1986, Soil development at Kongsfjorden, Spitsbergen: Polar Research, n.s., v. 4, p. 1–16.

Maxwell, J. B., 1980, The climate of the Canadian Arctic Islands and adjacent waters, Volume 1: Hull, Québec, Environment Canada, Atmospheric Environment Service, 531 p.

McGaw, R. W., Outcalt, S. I., and Ng, E., 1978, Thermal properties and regime of wet tundra soils at Barrow, Alaska, *in* Proceedings, International Conference on Permafrost, 3rd, Edmonton, Volume 1: Ottawa, National Research Council of Canada, p. 47–53.

Meinardus, W., 1912a, Beobachtungen über Detritussortierung und Strukturboden auf Spitzbergen: Gesellschaft für Erdkunde zu Berlin, Zeitschrift, v. 1912, p. 250–259.

Meinardus, W., 1912b, Über einige charakterische Bodenformen auf Spitzbergen, *in* Sitzungsberichte, Medizinischnaturwissenschaftliche Gesellschaft zu Münster i.w., Sitzung 26 Februar: Bonn, Naturhistorischer Verein der Preussische Rheinlande und Westfalens, p. 1–42.

Miethe, A., 1912, Über Karrebodenformen auf Spitzbergen: Gesellschaft für Erdkunde zu Berlin, Zeitschrift, v. 1912, p. 241–244.

Mohaupt, W., 1932, Beobachtungen über Bodenversetzungen und Kammeisbildungen aus dem Stubai und dem Grödener Tal [Ph.D. thesis]: Hamburg, University of Hamburg, Faculty of Mathematical and Natural Sciences, 69 p.

Mortensen, H., 1932, Über die physikalische Möglichkeit der "Brodel"-Hypothese: Centralblatt für Mineralogie, Geologie und Paläontologie, v. 1932, Abt. B, p. 417–422.

Mortensen, H., 1934, Bermerkungen: Centralblatt für Mineralogie, Geologie und Paläontologie, v. 1934, Abt. B, p. 45–46.

Nansen, F., 1922, Spitsbergen (third edition): Leipzig, F. A. Brockhaus, 327 p.

Nichols, R. L., 1953, Geomorphologic observations at Thule, Greenland and Resolute Bay, Cornwallis Island, N.W.T.: American Journal of Science, v. 251, p. 268–275.

Nicholson, F. H., 1976, Patterned ground formation and description as suggested by Low Arctic and Subarctic examples: Arctic and Alpine Research, v. 8, p. 329–342.

Nordenskjöld, O., 1907, Über die Natur der Polarländer. 2: Spitzbergen und die umliegenden Inseln: Geographische Zeitschrift, v. 13, p. 557–568.

NRCC/G National Research Council of Canada/Glossary. *See* Permafrost Subcommittee, 1988.

Outcalt, S. I., Nelson, F. E., and Hinkel, K. M., 1990, The zero-curtain effect: Heat and mass transfer across an isothermal region in freezing soil: Water Resources Research, v. 26, p. 1509–1515.

Palm, E., and Tweitereid, M., 1977, On patterned ground and free convection: Norsk Geografiska Tidsskrift, v. 31, p. 145–148.

Parmuzina, O. Yu., 1978, Kriogennoye stroenie i nektorye osobennosti l'dovydeleniya v sezonnotalum sloe, *in* Popov, A. I., ed., Problemy kriolitologii (Problems of cryolithology), Volume 7: Moscow, Moscow University Press, p. 141–164. (For English translation, see Parmuzina, 1980.)

Parmuzina, O. Yu., 1979, K voprosy o pereraspredelenii vlagi v merzlykh gruntakh (po naturnym nablyudeniyam) (An approach to the question of the redistribution of moisture in frozen soil [according to full-scale (field) observations]), *in* Popov, A. I., ed., Problemy kriolitologii (Problems of cryolithology), Volume 8: Moscow, Moscow University Press, p. 194–197.

Parmuzina, O. Yu., 1980, Cryogenic texture and some characteristics of ice formation in the active layer: Polar Geography and Geology, v. 4, p. 131–152. (Translation of Parmuzina, 1978.)

Paterson, T. H., 1940, The effects of frost action and solifluxion around Baffin Bay and in the Cambridge district: Geological Society of London Quarterly Journal, v. 96, part 1, p. 99–130.

Permafrost Subcommittee, 1988, Glossary of permafrost and related ground-ice terms: National Research Council of Canada Technical Memorandum 142, 156 p.

Pissart, A., 1966, Expériences et observations à propos de la genèse des sols polygonaux triés: Revue Belge de Géographie, v. 90, p. 55–73.

Pissart, A., 1972, Mouvements de sols gelés subissant des variations de température sous 0°: Résultats de mesures dilatométriques, *in* Adams, W. P., and Helleiner, F. M., eds., International Geography—La Géographie Internationale–1972, Proceedings, International Geographical Congress, 22nd, Montreal, Volume 1: Toronto, University of Toronto Press, p. 124–126.

Pissart, A., 1976, Sols à buttes, cercles non triés et sols striés non triés de l'île de Banks (Canada, N.W.T.): Biuletyn Peryglacjalny, no. 26, p. 275–285.

Pissart, A., 1982, Déformations de cylindres de limon entourés de graviers sous l'action d'alternances gel/dégel: Biuletyn Peryglacjalny, no. 29, p. 219–229.

Pissart, A., 1990, Advances in periglacial geomorphology: Zeitschrift für Geomorphologie, N.F., Supplementband, no. 79, p. 119–131.

Poser, H., 1931, Beiträge zur Kenntnis der arktischen Bodenformen: Geologische Rundschau, v. 22, p. 200–231.

Poser, H., 1933, Das Problem des Strukturbodens: Geologische Rundschau, v. 24, p. 105–121.

Ray, R. J., Krantz, W. B., Caine, T. N., and Gunn, R. D., 1983, A model for sorted patterned-ground regularity: Journal of Glaciology, v. 29, p. 317–337.

Rayleigh (Lord), 1916, On convection currents in a horizontal layer of fluid, when the higher temperature is on the under side: Philosophical Magazine and Journal of Science, 6th ser., v. 32, p. 529–546.

Repelewska-Pekalowa, J., and Gluza, A., 1988, Dynamics of permafrost active layer—Spitsbergen, *in* Senneset, K., ed., Proceedings, Permafrost International Conference, 5th, Trondheim, Norway, Volume 1: Trondheim, Norway, Tapir Publishers, p. 448–453.

Rieger, S., 1983, The genesis and classification of cold soils: New York, Academic Press, 230 p.

Rudberg, S., 1969, Distribution of small-scale periglacial and glacial geomorphological features on Axel Heiberg Island, Northwest Territories, Canada, *in* Péwé, T. L., ed., The periglacial environment: Montreal, McGill-Queens University Press, p. 129–159.

Rydquist, F., 1960, Studier inom Öländska polygonmarker: Ymer, p. 56–74. (Also published as Meddelande Geografiska Instituttet vid Stockholms Högskola, no. 125.)

Salomon, W., 1910, Die Spitzbergenfahrt des Internationalen Geologischen Kongresses: Geologische Rundschau, v. 1, p. 302–309.

Schenk, E., 1955, Die Mechanik der periglazialen Strukturboden: Hessischen Landesamtes für Bodenforschung, Abhandlungen, Heft 13, 92 p.

Schmertmann, J. H., and Taylor, R. S., 1965, Quantitative data from a patterned ground site over permafrost: U.S. Army Cold Regions Research and Engineering Laboratory Research Report 96, 76 p. + appendix.

Schunke, E., 1975, Die Periglazialerscheinungen Islands in Abhängigkeit von Klima und Substrat: Akademie der Wissenschaften zu Göttingen, Abhandlungen Mathematisch-Physikalische Klasse, Folge 3, 273 p.

Semmel, A., 1969, Verwitterungs- und Abtragungserscheinungen in rezenten Periglazialgebieten (Lappland und Spitzbergen): Würzburger Geographische Arbeiten, Heft 26, 82 p.

Sharp, R. P., 1942, Soil structures in the St. Elias Range, Yukon Territory: Journal of Geomorphology. v. 5, p. 274–301.

Shilts, W. W., 1973, Drift prospecting; geochemistry of eskers and till in permanently frozen terrain: District of Keewatin; Northwest Territories: Geological Survey of Canada Paper 72-45, 34 p.

Shilts, W. W., 1978, Nature and genesis of mudboils, central Keewatin, Canada: Canadian Journal of Earth Sciences, v. 15, p. 1053–1068.

Sletten, R. L., 1993, Laboratory simulation of dolomite and limestone dissolution: Rates, yield, and mineralogy of fine-grained residue, *in* Proceedings, Permafrost International Conference, 6th, Beijing, Volume 1: Wushan, Guangzhou, South China University of Technology Press, p. 580–585.

Smith, M. W., and Patterson, D. E., 1989, Detailed observations on the nature of frost heaving at a field scale: Canadian Geotechnical Journal, v. 26, p. 306–312.

Soil Survey Staff, 1975, Soil taxonomy—A basic system of soil classification for making and interpreting soil surveys: U.S. Department of Agriculture, Soil Conservation Service Agriculture Handbook 436, 754 p.

Sollid, J. L., and Sørbel, L., 1988, The area of Kvadehuksletta and Ny-Ålesund, *in* Orheim, A., and Sollid, J. L., eds., Svalbard Excursion Guide, Permafrost International Conference, 5th, Trondheim, Norway: Meddelelser fra Geografisk Institutt Oslo, Naturgeografisk Serie, Rapport 8, p. 54–60.

Sørensen, T., 1935, Bodenformen und Pflanzendecke in Nordostgrönland: Meddelelser om Grønland, v. 93, 69 p.

Sumgin, M. I., 1931, Usloviya pochvoobrazovaniya v oblasti vechnoi merzloty (Conditions of soil formation in the region of the "Ever Frozen Layer"): Pochvovedenie, v. 26, p. 5–17. (English summary, p. 16–17.)

Swanson, L. E., and Rothwell, R. L., 1986, Thawing of ground frost on a drained and undrained boreal wetland site, *in* Kane, D. L., ed., Proceedings, Cold Regions Hydrology Symposium, Fairbanks: American Water Resources Association Technical Publication Series TPS-861, p. 231–236.

Taber, S., 1943, Perennially frozen ground in Alaska: Its origin and history: Geological Society of America Bulletin, v. 54, p. 1433–1548.

Tarnocai, C., 1976, Soils of Bathurst, Cornwallis, and adjacent islands, District of Franklin: Geological Survey of Canada Paper 76-1B, p. 137–141.

Tarnocai, C., 1980, Summer temperatures of cryosolic soils in the north-central Keewatin, N.W.T.: Canadian Journal of Soil Science, v. 60, p. 311–327.

Tedrow, J. C. F., and Krug, E. C., 1982, Weathered limestone accumulations in the High Arctic: Biuletyn Peryglacjalny, no. 29, p. 143–146.

Thom, G., 1981, Patterned ground in South Georgia, Antarctica [Ph.D. thesis]: Aberdeen, Scotland, University of Aberdeen, 178 p.

Thorsteinsson, R., 1958, Cornwallis and Little Cornwallis Islands, District of Franklin, Northwest Territories: Geological Survey of Canada Memoir 294, 134 p.

Thorsteinsson, R., 1986, Geology of Cornwallis Island and neighbouring smaller islands, Canadian Arctic Archipelago, District of Franklin, Northwest Territories: Geological Survey of Canada Map 1626A, scale 1:250,000.

Thorsteinsson, R., and Kerr, J. W., 1968, Cornwallis Island and adjacent smaller islands, Canadian Arctic Archipelago: Geological Survey of Canada Paper 67-64, 16 p.

Vandenberghe, J., 1988, Cryoturbations, *in* Clark, M. J., ed., Advances in periglacial geomorphology: New York, John Wiley & Sons, p. 179–198.

Vandenberghe, J., 1992, Cryoturbations: A sediment structural analysis: Permafrost and Periglacial Processes, v. 3, p. 343–352.

Van Vliet-Lanoë, B., 1983, Études cryopédologiques au sud du Kongsfjord-Svalbard: Centre de Géomorphologie du C.N.R.S. [Centre National de la Recherche Scientifique], G.I.S. Arctique, Publication interne, 39 p.

Van Vliet-Lanoë, B., 1985, Frost effects in soils, *in* Boardman, J., ed., Soils of Quaternary landscape evolution: London, John Wiley & Sons Ltd., p. 117–158.

Van Vliet-Lanoë, B., 1988a, Le rôle de la glace de ségrégation dans les formations superficielles de l'Europe de l'Ouest—Processus et héritages [Thèse de Doctorat d'État]: Université de Paris I-Sorbonne, Centre de Géomorphologie du C.N.R.S. [Centre National de la Recherche Scientifique], 2 volumes, 854 p.

Van Vliet-Lanoë, B., 1988b, The significance of cryoturbation phenomena in environmental reconstruction: Journal of Quaternary Science, v. 3, p. 85–96.

Van Vliet-Lanoë, B., 1988c, The origin of patterned grounds in N.W. Svalbard, *in* Senneset, K., ed., Proceedings, Permafrost International Conference, 5th, Trondheim, Norway, Volume 2: Trondheim, Norway, Tapir Publishers, p. 1008–1013.

Van Vliet-Lanoë, B., 1989a, Aspects dynamiques de versants de gélifraction en milieu arctique—Exemples du Kongsfjord, Spitzberg du Nord-Ouest: Comité National Français de Géographie, Commission pour l'Étude des Phénomènes Périglaciaires, Notes et Comptes-rendus de Groupe de Travail "Regionalisation du Périglaciaire," Fasc. 14, p. 75–82.

Van Vliet-Lanoë, B., 1989b, Refreezing ice and patterned ground in Svalbard, *in* Stäblein, G., ed., Polar geomorphology, International Conference on Geomorphology, 2nd, Symposium No. 5, Abstracts and Papers: Bremen, Universität Bremen, Studiengang Geographie, Materialien und Manuscripte, v. 17, p. 56–58.

Van Vliet-Lanoë, B., 1991, Differential frost heave, loadcasting and convection: Converging mechanisms: A discussion of the origin of cryoturbations: Permafrost and Periglacial Processes, v. 2, p. 123–139.

Van Vliet-Lanoë, B., and Coutard, J. P., 1986, *in* Lautridou, J. P., Osouf, J. C., Van Vliet-Lanoë, B., and Coutard, J. P., À propos de deux thèmes de recherche abordés au Centre de Géomorphologie du C.N.R.S.: Biuletyn Peryglacjalny, no. 31, p. 190–198.

Vasil'yevskaya, V. D., 1979, Generic characteristics of soils in a spotty tundra: Soviet Soil Science, no. 4, p. 390–401. (Translated from Pochvovedenie, 1979, v. 7, p. 20–32.)

Veillette, J. J., 1980, Nonsorted circles in cohesionless fine silty sand, north-central District of Keewatin: Geological Survey of Canada Paper 80-1B, p. 259–267.

Washburn, A. L., 1950, Patterned ground: Revue Canadienne de Géographie, no. 3-4, p. 5–59.

Washburn, A. L., 1956, Classification of patterned ground and review of suggested origins: Geological Society of America Bulletin, v. 67, p. 823–865.

Washburn, A. L., 1969, Weathering, frost action, and patterned ground in the Mesters Vig district, Northeast Greenland: Meddelelser om Grønland, v. 176, 303 p.

Washburn, A. L., 1979, Geocryology—A survey of periglacial processes and environments: London, Edward Arnold, 402 p. (New York, Halsted Press, 1980).

Washburn, A. L., 1989, Near-surface soil displacement in sorted circles, Resolute area, Cornwallis Island, Canadian High Arctic: Canadian Journal of Earth Sciences, v. 26, p. 941–955.

Washburn, A. L., 1991, Plugs: Origin and transitions to some associated forms of patterned ground, Cornwallis Island, Canadian High Arctic, *in* Periglacial Geomorphology, Annual Geomorphology Symposium, 22nd, Program and Abstracts: Buffalo, State University of New York, p. 11–12. (Omitted from subsequently published edition.)

Washburn, A. L., Sanders, J. E., and Flint, R. F., 1963, A convenient nomenclature for poorly sorted sediments: Journal of Sedimentary Petrology, v. 33, p. 478–480. (A loose-leaf note, missing in some copies, combines the most abundant components of a term as a compound noun if differing by less that 5%.)

Washburn, A. L., and Stuiver, M., 1985, Radiocarbon dates from Cornwallis Island area, Arctic Canada—an interim report: Canadian Journal of Earth Sciences, v. 22, p. 630–637.

Wassén, G., 1965, Lost and living lakes in the upper Ume Valley, *in* The plant cover of Sweden: Acta Phytogeographica Suecia 50 (Uppsala, Almqvist & Wiksell), p. 233–239.

Wassén, G., 1966, Gardiken, Vegetation und Flora eines lappländischen Seeufers: Kungliga Svenska Vetenskapsakademiens Avhandlingar i Naturskyddsärenden 22 (Stockholm, Almqvist & Wiksell), 142 p.

White, S. E., 1976, Is frost action really only a hydration shattering? A review: Arctic and Alpine Research, v. 8, p. 1–6.

White, T. L., and Williams, P. J., 1994, Cryogenic alteration of frost susceptible soils, *in* Frémond, M., ed., Ground freezing 94: Proceedings of the Seventh International Symposium on Ground Freezing, Nancy, France, 1994: Rotterdam, A. A. Balkema, p. 17–24.

Williams, P. J., and Smith, M. W., 1989, The frozen earth: Fundamentals of geocryology: Cambridge, Cambridge University Press, Studies in Polar Research, 306 p.

Woo, M.-K, and Steer, P., 1982, Occurrence of surface flow on arctic slopes, southwestern Cornwallis Island: Canadian Journal of Earth Sciences, v. 19, p. 2368–2377.

Woo, M.-K., and Steer, P., 1983, Slope hydrology as influenced by thawing of the active layer, Resolute, N.W.T.: Canadian Journal of Earth Sciences, v. 20, p. 978–986.

Woo, M.-K., and Xia, Z., 1995, Suprapermafrost groundwater seepage in gravelly terrain, Resolute, NWT, Canada: Permafrost and Periglacial Proceses, v. 6, p. 57–72.

Woo, M.-K., and Xia, Z., 1996, Effects of hydrology on the thermal conditions of the active layer: Nordic Hydrology, v. 27, p. 129–142.

Wright, W. R., and Foss, J. E., 1968, Movement of silt-sized particles in sand columns: Soil Science Society of America Proceedings, v. 32, p. 446–448.

Zhestkova, T. N., 1978, Resultaty ekhsperimental'nykh issledovaniy protsessa promerzania tonkodispersnykh gruntov (Results of experimental studies of the freezing process in the very fine-grained soils), *in* Proceedings, International Conference on Permafrost, 3rd, Edmonton, Volume 1: Ottawa, National Research Council of Canada, p. 156–162.

Zhestkova, T. N., 1980, Results of experimental studies of the freezing process in very fine-grained soils, *in* English translations of the forty-nine Soviet papers, the one French paper, and the three invited Soviet theme papers, Part 1, International Conference on Permafrost, 3rd, Edmonton, 1978: Ottawa, National Research Council of Canada, NRCC 18119, p. 119–136.

Zhu, C., Cui, Z.-J., Xiong, H.-G., and Yao, Z., 1993, Characteristics of the permafrost structure on the Fildes Peninsula, King George Island, Antarctica: Science in China, ser. B, v. 36, p. 997–1010.

Manuscript Accepted by the Society August 6, 1996

Index

[Italic page numbers indicate major references]

T

U

V

W

Z

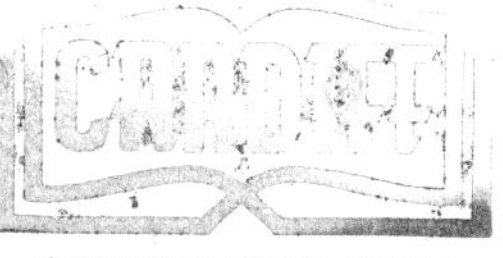